Repair and Strengthening of OLD STEEL TRUSS BRIDGES

Prepared by the
Task Committee on Strength of Old Truss Bridges
of the Working Committee on Safety of Bridges
under the Technical Committee on
Structural Safety and Reliability

B. Bakht
R. A. P. Sweeney
W. W. Saunders
R. B. Yule
W. G. Byers
F. Moses
W. T. McKeel
M. Higgins
L. Kahn
C. P. Heins, Chairman

AMERICAN SOCIETY OF CIVIL ENGINEERS FOUNDED 1852

Published by
American Society of Civil Engineers
345 East 47th Street
New York, New York 10017

Price: $9.00

TABLE OF CONTENTS

Page

I. INTRODUCTION AND HISTORY

During the early 1900's, numerous pin jointed steel bridge trusses were constructed throughout the United States. In the intervening years, these trusses were replaced by major structures in the metropolitan area. However, in the rural areas, these bridges still remain and are functional, despite the increased traffic volumes. The Federal Highway Administration reports that nationally, there are 6900 bridges that are classified as being structurally deficient and 26,600 functionally obsolete. The highway engineer therefore, is faced with the problem of maintaining and upgrading these structures, as the cost of replacement as a group would be excessive.

This paper therefore will present information relative to the rating and strengthening of such bridges, in order to guide the engineer in deciding various alternatives in bridge rehabilitation or replacement.

Most of the old highway truss bridges, which are structurally deficient, have spans lengths under 150 feet. Most of them also have narrow roadways, and in many instances should be replaced because of the traffic hazard and one way traffic restriction.

In the range of spans up to 150 feet, the Pratt truss (with parallel chords and inclined end posts) was used extensively. The multiple intersection trusses like the Whipple, Bollman and Fink and the single intersection Warren and Howe were rarely used.

The pony truss (no top lateral system) was not used extensively until heavier loads and wider roadways caused the use of deeper and heavier floor beams. With the deeper floor beam as an anchor, outriggers were built from the end of the floor beam and carried up to the top chord, which thus provided bracing of the top chord against buckling.

The charge of this committee by its very title "Repair and Strengthening of Old Steel Truss Bridges" will encompass structures built prior to 1920. At about that time the state highway systems were developing a uniform design criteria approved by the American Association of State Highway Officials (AASHO). Actual truck axle loads and an equivalent uniform load for long spans were then specified. Counties and cities eventually adopted the code and a bridge with glaringly deficient load capacity was rarely built after that time.

Previous to the organization of state highway systems and AASHTO, the construction of bridges was in the hands of counties and cities and the resulting product was quite diverse.

County and city officials and their staffs generally used Bridge Companies for the design and construction of bridges. These so-called Bridge Companies were on call from the county or city officials and made proposals to design and erect a bridge. These companies usually designed and fabricated the steel superstructure and some times erected it on a foundation provided by others. Competition was keen and stories abound about the operation of this system. In any case, the bridge company designed and fabricated the bridge in their own shop. Design was quite simple by present standards and by tradition for many years the design load was on the basis of pounds per square foot of floor surface. This was probably applied to the floor as well as the trusses but possibly not in the same magnitude. In any case with the advent of the automobile and particularly the truck, for a one load on the bridge, the stringers and floor beams have much less capacity than the trusses. A stringer must be designed to carry its part of wheel load and a floor beam one axle load. This is much greater than the uniform load of a herd of cattle, which by tradition was the criteria in some cases.

Since riveting was strictly a shop art in the area of the old steel bridge, the shop fabrication was designed for field erection with no riveting and no sophisticated erection equipment. The trusses were pin connected and all the field connections were bolted.

Details of the various elements of such bridges will be given in the following Section 2.

In general, the consensus of the State Departments of Transportation is that these old metal truss bridges are functionally obsolete and that repair and strengthening are undertaken to add a few more years of service until the bridges can be replaced.

2. DESCRIPTION OF TRUSS BRIDGES

2.1 Floor Systems

Where the depth of the floor system is not critical, the deck usually is supported on two or more lines of longitudinal stringers, resting on the top flange of the transverse floor beams , which are usually hung from the bottom chord pins at the truss panel points with an inverted stirrup. Where end floor beams are used, they are normally connected at the end panel points. In some designs, the stringers in the end panels are supported directly on the piers or abutments and a strut connects the trusses at the ends of the span. A number of highway trusses with timber floors have timber stringers resting on the top flanges of the floor beams (11).

Where a minimum depth floor is desired, closely spaced transverse beams may be supported by longitudinal girders suspended from the lower joints of the trusses as shown in Figure 1.

The deck may consist of timbers concrete slab, metal grating on highway bridges, or ties laid directly on the stringers of railway spans. Creosoted blocks were often used for highway bridges floors in and near cities for riding quality and reduced noise.

2.2 Truss Elements

The older steel truss spans are more likely to be pin-connected than riveted. The most common configuration is a Pratt truss with counters in one or more panels near midspan. The Warren truss is generally used for short to moderate span riveted trusses but, except for moveable spans, this type of construction was not generally used before about 1920. A few Whipple trusses and occasional examples of other configurations are still in use.

The re-erection of railway spans has been a relatively common practice. The capacity of spans designed for light loading has been increased by re-erecting two identical spans together with two trusses on each side of the track. In one system, shown in Figure 2, new floor beams were suspended from brackets attached to the posts of each pair of trusses as shown in Figure 3, and all stringers from the original spans reused to double the capacity of the floor system. In the compression chord member, the top chord and the batter posts, were usually two channels with their backs facing inward; a cover plate on the top side and riveted lacing on the bottom. The tension members were eye bars. The pins had nuts on their ends, tightened against a shoulder. They were rarely keyed. Quite often due to forward rotation of the abutment the last two panels of lower chord were slack. Diagonal bracing in the plane of the top chord and the floor beams consisted of rods tightened by nuts at their ends.

Representative long span trusses are described in reference (2), but because of their limited number, are of less interest than the more common shorter spans.

The top chords and end posts of steel trusses for railroad bridges usually consist of two vertical plates and four angles with lacing bars connecting the lower angles and solid cover plates or lacing bars on the top of the member. For shorter spans or lighter loads, rolled channels may be used instead of the vertical plates with angles at the corners of the members. Very heavily loaded members may have additional vertical plates to provide increased cross sectional area. Riveted fabrication of compression members is, for all practical purposes, universal in the older trusses. Pin plates may be used to provide additional bearing area at pins. Stay plates replace lacing bars at the ends of members.

Lower chords may consist entirely of built up members in either continuous through two panels at each end of the truss may be combined with eye bar members for the lower chords in interior panels. Built up lower chords may consist of two channels or two pairs of angles connected with lacing bars or batten plates. Wide flanged sections may be used in riveted trusses.

Built up web members carrying compression typically consist of two channels connected with lacing bars. The flanges of the channels are often turned out to facilitate fabrication. Four angles arranged in a square and connected with lacing bars are sometimes used for lightly loaded compression members. Tension members may consist of two angles or pairs of angles with batten plates or lacing connecting the angles or pairs or of two pairs of angles and a continuous plate in the form of an I section. Wide flanged sections have been used as web members in riveted spans. Heavily loaded members may consist of plate and angle sections similar to chord sections. Eye bar members are often used as diagonals and counters in pin-connected Pratt trusses. Counters are typically provided with turnbuckles for adjustment.

2.3 Bearings

Pin-connected truss spans are typically supported on bearings connected to the trusses by the pins connecting the lower chords to the end posts. This arrangement automatically allows rotation due to deflection of the trusses under load. Changes in the length of the lower chord caused by live load deflection or temperature change must be accomodated by the expansion bearings. Fixed bearings need only allow rotation of the truss and distribute the reaction over an area sufficient to prevent overstressing the bearing area of the substructure. The bearings of the heavier riveted truss spans are connected to the trusses by pins at or near the intersection of the end posts and lower chords. Light, short spans may have simpler arrangements.

Expansion bearings consist of rockers or roller nests. A single rocker may be attached to the pin at the end of the truss. Greater capacity is provided by two parallel rockers supporting a shoe attached to the pin at the end of the truss. A nest of rollers between the shoe and masonry plate is a common type of expansion bearing. The rollers may be complete circular cylinders or segments of cylinders as shown in figure 4. Segmental rollers provide more lines of contact in a given bearing length than cylindrical rollers with the same radius. Provision is normally made to prevent lateral movement of expansion bearings. Short, light spans may have sliding expansion bearings.

2.4 Critical Members

Not all elements of a truss span are equally important to the behavior of the span. Verticals at the panel points of a thru Warren truss where the diagonals intersect at the lower chord serve only to transfer the floor beam reactions to the lower joint and stiffen the upper chord. They carry no primary stress from dead load or live load. The post at mid-span of a Pratt truss with an even number of panels and counters in trusses wtih eye bar diagonals are loaded only when an unsymmetrical live load overcomes the dead load shear in the panels involved.

Chord members and end posts are critical to the stability of the span. With the exception of floor beam hangers, the importance of web members increases from mid-span to the end of the span. In some instances, a continuous floor system will carry load in spite of the loss of a hanger or will pick up load that would normally be carried by a damaged chord.

Redundancy in the entire span, in a sub-system or in an individual member increases the reliability of the span. If a floor system has only two stringers per panel, failure of one stringer will certainly cause collapse of a timber floor and probably, of a concrete floor. Additional stringers provide reserve strength. The failure of one eye bar in a two eye bar member and resulting pin rotation is blamed for the Point Pleasant Bridge ("Silver Bridge") failure (7). It has been noted (4) that the reliability of an eye bar member is increased by increasing the number of bars in the member when the total cross sectional area of the member is held constant and that the crack limiting characteristics of riveted girders produce sizeable reductions in the probability of failure due to tension flange cracks when the number of cover plates is increased without increasing the net flange area.

3. INSPECTION AND DEFECTS

3.1 Inspection Procedures

The evaluation of any existing structure, especially one that has been in service for a period of time, requires a determination of its physical condition which can be obtained only by an adequate inspection. Since inspection involves the determination of physical quantities, the data obtained are never exact. Increased care will reduce the magnitude of error but, unless the procedure is biased, both over and under estimates of the size of defects and other significant measurements will occur. Various aspects of inspection are discussed in the literature (3, 4, 8, 9, 15).

The key to successful and efficient inspection is concentration on the areas where serious defects are most probable. These include areas where stability requirements or high stresses as determined by analysis make nearly all detectable defects serious and areas where the service history of similar structures indicates a relatively high probability of sizable defects. The past environment of the structure, including both the loading history and the amount of exposure to corrosive influences, can determine the types of defect most likely to occur.

Except for the effects of the incidental redundancy not usually considered in design such as multiple eye bars in a single member, the crack-limiting characteristics of riveted built-up members and the participation of floor systems with chords, the analysis of stability and stresses and indentification of critical members in any particular span can be accomplished by ordinary methods.

Certain locations should receive particular attention, even in members subjected to only moderate stresses. Repair details are often determined by expediency and may include an increase in section where under-sized components were used, misaligned compression members and stress raisers such as undercut welds across tension members (4). The distribution of load in two-channel floor beam hangers is related to the method of connecting the channels by the use of lacing bars resulting in a much better distribution than batten plates (12, 16). Details that have caused problems are described in the literature (6, 10) and will be discussed in connnection with the appropriate parts of the span.

Under most conditions, visual observation will provide the primary inspection and will be supplemented by other methods only where the results of the visual observations indicate the desirability of more sophisticated methods. A preliminary examination should be made before removing dirt, rust, paint or other surface coatings as cracks in the coating or rust stains may reveal cracks in the metal underneath. Once cleaning is started, it must be continued until all surface coatings are removed in the area to be inspected. If a structure is to be painted, particularly if it is to be cleaned by sandblasting, the period between cleaning and painting, when the metal is nearly or completely bare and scaffolds provide access, is the most efficient time for inspection.

Measurements should be made as required to determine both the cross section and alignment of all members. The locations of all measurements and the locations and descriptions of all defects should be reported.

As a rule, the results of the inspection should be reported on a standard form. Typical inspection record forms are illustrated in the literature (3, 9) and in Table 1. The form should include identification of the bridge, its location and consist, other pertinent general information, checklist to aid in preventing oversights, adequate space for describing defects and recording other information obtained in the inspection and space to show the indentity of the inspector and date of inspection.

If the material in the span cannot be determined from plans, it can often be identified by spark testing or filing to reveal the slag inclusions in wrought iron (4). Hardness tests can provide additional information. In some cases, tensile tests on samples obtained from the span will be justified but care must be exercised in selecting the locations from which samples are taken as this is not a non-destructive procedure.

Although rare, there are environments where considerable corrosion loss can occur without obvious pitting or rust accumulation. Therefore, if plan dimensions are to be used for the thickness of members, actual thickness should be determined, regardless of appearance, at enough locations to verify the plan dimensions in addition to those locations where there is obvious section loss.

The existance of cracks can be verified and their length defined with liquid penetrant. Penetrant systems packaged in aerosol cans are useful for this work and for detailed inspection of small areas for cracks open to the surface. Maximum sensitivity is obtained by subjecting the structure to loading that will cause cracks to open during the penetration period and again after the developer is applied.

A system of ultrasonic crack detection now under development promises to provide capabilities for inspecting the heads of eye bars for cracks originating at the pin holes which are inaccessible to other inspection methods (1).

The behavior of the span under traffic should be observed even if a more complete program of field testing is not considered justifiable. The observation under traffic should include, among other items, apparent deflection, sidesway, behavior of counters, the point at which loose eye bars pick up load, the behavior of bearings, bowing of compression members and any tendency of observed cracks to open under load.

Although not serious in itself, except for possible effects on secondary stresses, a loss of camber is an indication of changes in the truss that may have been detrimental. The most probable causes are wear at pinned joints, yielding under past overload or a major increase in dead load. Unless compared to camber data at the time of erection, a relative lack of camber may not indicate a loss of camber.

3.2 Floor Systems

Neglecting the deck, the most common defects in floor systems are corrosion and cracking. If the deck is not watertight, corrosion is aggrevated by drainage from the deck which may have contained de-icing salts, brine from refrigerator cars or other corrosive materials. In addition, complete drying is usually slow. Cracking is likely to be caused by longitudinal forces at stringer to floor beam connections resulting from chord elongation and stringer continuity, high local stresses due to loss of section in severly corroded areas and details that produce stress concentration or anti-plane shear and bending.

Corrosion is likely to cause loss of section in top flanges of stringers and floor beams, in bottom flanges where laterals are in contact with the flanges, in the webs of floor beams above stringer flanges or erection seat angles and in the webs of stringers above horizontal diaphragms. Where floor beam flange angles end at the edge of floor beam connection angles with only the web available to carry longitudinal forces between the two, cracking due to anti-plane (Mode III) shear is fairly common. Cutouts in floor beam webs to allow for placing coverplates across the tops of adjacent stringers or stringers and brackets at end floor beams, can cause stress concentration and cracking. Vertical angles connecting stringers to floor beams or connecting longitudinal girders to truss members may develop cracks in the angle fillets or through rivet holes in the legs where rivets are loaded in tension. Cracks in stringer webs may occur at the tops or bottoms of vertical welded diaphragms due to anti-plane bending caused by differences in stringer deflections. In old highway bridges on secondary roads, the end panel of stringers are often overstressed by the impact of trucks bouncing over the abutment backwall onto the bridge floors. In this case, the stringers show permanent deflection and the floor may be loose. Other specific cases of floor system failures are described in references (6, 10).

3.3 Truss Elements

The inspection of truss elements should include careful examination for evidence of collision damage and thorough inspection of any repairs. Typical collision damage includes local bending or tearing of projecting elements such as flanges, buckling of lacing bars associated with bending of built up members, overall bending of members which causes eccentricity, local bending of individual elements of built up members with a resulting sizeable reduction in radius of gyration and sharp notches produced by cuts in compact members such as eye bars.

Corrosion can cause both a reduction of area and, where rust build up causes buldging of coverplates between rivets, reduction in the ultimate capacity of built up compression members produced by loss of plate effectiveness due to local eccentricity and buckling of the plate.

Unequal loading of eye bars in a member with consequent overloading of some bars is caused by maladjustment due to pin wear and by reduction of effective length produced by bending from collisions. Inspection and repairs are discussed in reference (14).

Floor beam hangers are subject to fatigue failures at copes and pin plate rivet holes (8,10). Blacksmith welds where threaded rods for turnbuckles are forged to eye bars and the eyes of eye bars formed by bending the bar around a pin a forging instead of upsetting and boring may also be points of weakness (5).

3.4 Bearings

Complete failure of one or more bearings will result in dropping one end of the span or in general instability. Less extreme conditions such as siezing or misalignment will considerably alter behavior of the span causing unplanned stress distributions and, possibly, distress in main truss members. Bent or broken anchor bolts are an indication of bearing problems. Corrosion of rocker pins will cause siezing. Accumulations of dirt or debris under rollers or rockers can prevent movement of expansion bearings. Masonry plates under roller nests of heavily loaded spans may become worn to a degree that prevents proper movement. If nests of segmental rollers are out of adjustment, the movement may be limited by the flat sides of the rollers coming into contact with each other. Extreme movement of rockers can result in overturning. Siezing of rocker pins can shift the reaction on the span to the edge of the shoe causing local failure in the span.

3.5 Connections

Connections are often the location of distress. Broken or loose rivets are common. The shanks of bolts may be considerably reduced by a combination of rust and wear. Corrosion and wear of pins and pin holes can extremely affect performance. The surfaces of pin holes may be highly stressed and are rarely accessable for inspection. Connection angles are frequently cracked in the fillet or through rivet holes in the leg where rivets may be loaded in tension.

Loose rivets may be indicated by paint cracks or rust stains. A more positive method for detecting loose rivets involves tapping one side of a rivet head with a light hammer then tapping from the other side while holding a washer against the opposite side of the head as shown in Figure 6. Movement of a loose rivet can be felt through the washer.

Connections may be detailed in a manner that traps water causing severe local corrosion. Moisture between adjacent eye bar heads has cuased section loss. Water may also be trapped where portal angles frame into the sides of the end posts.

4. ANALYTICAL PROCEDURES FOR RATING OF TRUSSES

A comprehensive and critical review of all the available relevent methods of analysis, although very desirable, is not attempted here. Only the commonly employed methods and practices and those which were found to be useful by the authors of this report, are mentioned here.

4.1 Floor Systems

For the analysis of the floor systems, it is sufficiently accurate to assume that the floor is rigidly supported against vertical deflections at its points of connection with the trusses. Neglect of the interaction between the floor system and trusses results in slightly conservative answers but the degree of this conservatism is so small as not to warrant the extra effort to account for the interaction in the analysis.

Floor Beams

Usually floor beams, for the sake of analysis, are isolated from the rest of the floor systems. In floor systems with stringers, the vehicl loads are first statically transferred onto stringers and then the stringer reactions are treated as concentrated loads on the floor beams. In the absense of stringers, the wheel loads are transferred to the floor beams through unit width strips of the deck. Thus no account is taken of the dispersion of loads. Such an approach results in gross over-estimation of moment in the floor beams. A comparison of the floor beam moment as obtained by rigorous analysis of the floor system using grillage analogy and by the above mentioned simplified approach, is shown in Figure 6. It can be seen that the simplified approach results in over-estimation of the maximum moment by about 25%, in the case of a concrete deck or a similar tape deck.

In the absense of more realistic methods, such as finite elements on grillage analogy methods, the loads can be assumed to disperse at an angle of 45°, as shown in Figure 6.c. Thus a load P which was transferred as a concentrated load of intensity $P(L-\ell_1)/L$ to the floor beam (Figure 6b) would now be transferred as a uniformly distributed load of length $2\ell_1$ with a total weight of $P(L-\ell_1)/L$. The floor beams moments obtained by this approach are plotted in Figure 6. It can be seen that while this approach still results in conservative answers, the margin of error is considerably reduced.

Stringers

Distribution of wheel loads on stringers are obtained by assuming that the floor beams provide full restraint against vertical deflections. With this assumption, the distribution of wheel loads is accounted for by the AASHTO criteria for distribution of loads. A recently developed method by Bakht (17) in which the simplicity of the current AASHTO method is still maintained, solutions are obtained which are comparable to those obtained by computer based methods.

The assumption of the floor beams providing full restraint against vertical deflections results in over-estimation of moments in stringers as shown in Figure 8. A more realistic analysis would require consideration of the floor beams as a part of the system. Unfortunately, simple methods of analysis do not remain applicable if the floor beams are to be considered in the calculations. For a realistic assessment of live load moments in stringers, computer based methods such as grillage analogy (23, 36) and finite elements (22) should be used. In many cases, the stringers are in fact continuous from panel to panel under actual loads, although designed as simply supported. In spite of their performance at working loads, they may prove to behave as simply supported at ultimate load.

Concrete Deck Slabs

Extensive testing of laboratory models of concrete deck slabs and and deck slabs of existing bridges; Batchelor, B. deV., Hewitt, B. E. (24, 25, 26, 27, 28, 30) has established the punching shear failure as the primary failure made for these concrete slabs. It was found that the ultimate strength of concrete deck slabs, which was considerably more than generally believed, was only slightly affected by the amount of reinforcement in the slab. Batchelor et al.(29) have developed a computer program to determine the true ultimate strength of concrete slabs. Values of the minimum strength of concrete slabs having 0.2% reinforcement and span (i.e. spacing of stringers) of 12' as calculated by this program are shown in Table 2. The strength is given in terms of the maximum concentrated load (in kips) representing the foot print of one set of wheels (constituting half the axle weight) of the design vehicle. The thickness of the slab in Table 2 refers to the overall slab thickness where there is no evidence of spalling but in case of deteriorated slabs, it refers to the minimum thickness of sound concrete in the slab. The concrete strength increases by a small margin with the increase in reinforcement percentage. The decrease of span, however, has a considerable influence in increasing the ultimate strength of the slab. Full set of Tables can be found in Section 14 of the forthcoming Ontario Highway Bridge Design Code, the development of which is discussed by Dorton and Csagoly (35).

Timber Decks

AASHTO recommendations for distributing a wheel load over a width of 20 inches for HS20 loading is quite realistic for nail laminated transverse decks. During the first two years or so of service, the distribution is much better than suggested by the AASHTO recommended value but after that the nails become loose, thus eliminating the interaction between the adjacent laminates. As a result of this only those laminates which are directly below the wheel sustain its load.

4.2 Trusses

The force analysis of trusses is usually limited to the determination of member axial forces, which are obtained on the assumption that the truss members are interconnected through pin connections. In most steel trusses (except Pratts and pin connected Warrens) the members are rigidly connected together by gusset plates and fasteners so that the end of a member cannot freely rotate with respect to other members meeting at the joint. In reality, any rotation is accompanied by a restraint jointly provided by other members meeting at the joint. Such rotational restraint, because of the large difference between the ridigities of individual members and that of the overall truss, has little influence on the member axial forces and, therefore, can be neglected during the force analysis. In some trusses the lateral bracing system and floor system participate with the truss in carrying load thus reducing the axial forces in the members of the truss.

Presence of relatively slender compression members in trusses makes a separate strength analysis of the truss an essential part of the evaluation process. Unlike many other bridge structures, the ultimate strength of trusses cannot be realistically projected directly from the results of elastic force analysis. The joint rotational restraints, which are quite justificably neglected during th- force analysis, have considerable influence on the ultimate load carrying capacity of a truss. The usual practive of considering each member to be pin connected at each of its ends for the purpose of establishing the buckling load of a member, is very conservative and results in unnecessarily large margins of safety. Some methods of realistically determining the ultimate load carrying capacity of trusses are discussed in Sections 4.2.1 and 4.2.2.

4.2.1 Truss Buckling

In-Plane Buckling

With the increase of axial loads, the rotational stiffness at the end of a compression members decreases and that of a tension member increases, although at a slower rate. When the combined rotational stiffness provided by all members meeting at a joint becomes zero or negative, the joint becomes unstable, causing the failure of the truss in its own plane. A truss can also buckle in its plane through the instability of one of its compression members. For determining the buckling loads for joints and individual members, it is necessary to correctly estimate the rotational stiffnesses of joints.

The rotational stiffness of a joint, which is a non-linear function of the applied load, cannot be determined without considering the influence of all the members of the truss, in which case the problem become too large to be easily solved by manual means. Csagoly and Bakht (19) have presented a computer oriented iteration technique for determining the rotational stiffness of joints for different levels of loads and also to determine the critical loads for joint or individual member instability. The method considers the interaction of rigidities of all joints in the framework.

Hoff et al. (20) and Bolton (18) have proposed manual iteration methods for determining the critical loads at which any one of the truss joints would become unstable. The process basically consists of applying a unit moment at a joint and distributing it through the truss by the moment distribution method employing carry over factors which are modified to reflect the presence of axial loads. The joint is declared as having become unstable when the moment begins to diverge. The method cannot be used for predicting the critical loads for individual compression members, which may govern the strength of the whole truss.

Out-of-Plane Buckling

When the compression chords of a truss are not supported laterally by bracings in the horizontal plane, as in the case of half through or pony trusses, the strength of the truss is usually governed by the out-of-plane buckling of the compression chord. The compression chord in these trusses are elastically supported by outstanding vertical members which are rigidly connected to the floor beams. AASHTO specifications (1973) specify that the outstanding verticals, the floor beams and their mutual connections be designed to resist a lateral force of at least 300 pounds per linear foot applied to the top chord panel points. In addition, the compression chord is required to be designed as a column with elastic lateral supports.

The out-of-plane buckling loads of the compression chord are, according to the 1973 AASHTO recommendations, calculated by formulae for columns on elastic supports as given by Timoshenko and Gere (21). The formulae assume the top chord to be a straight column, hinged at the two ends, supported continuously by an elastic medium and subjected to a parabolic compressive force which has a zero value at the support and a maximum at mid length. The assumptions on which these formulae are based are at variance with the actual conditions, therefore, the formulae cannot be expected to provide realistic solutions. The discrepancies in the above mentioned assuptions and actual conditions are as follows.

a. The top end chords of pony trusses in North American are not straight, as they usually are in Europe. They have inclined end chords as shown in Figure 9.

b. The outstanding verticals provide discrete lateral elastic supports rather than a continuous elastic medium.

c. Actual forces, especially those due to live loads, in the compression chord are quite different from the assumed forces (see Figure 7).

d. The outstanding verticals besides providing the lateral elastic supports also laterally deflect the top chord. This lateral deflection, which depends upon the loads on the floor beams and considerably influences the lateral buckling load of the chord, is not accounted for in the Timoshenko and Gere formulae.

Csagoly and Bakht (34) have developed a method for determining the lateral buckling loads of pony trusses. The method, because of being computer based, eliminates the over-simplifying assumptions inherent in the Timoshenko (1961) method and provides realistic solutions. The validity of the method has been checked through tests on laboratory models and a full scale ultimate load test (17).

4.2.2 Local Buckling

Solutions for buckling problems assume that a compression member acts as one unit and that, if it is made up of several components, it will not fail "prematurely" through the local failure of a component. In reality, compression members are often made up of several components and, depending upon the manner in which the components are joined together, are susceptible to local failure.

An ultimate load test on a steel truss bridge (17) showed that the weakest link in the strength of the whole truss was a coverplate in a built-up compression chord. Accumulation of rust between the coverplate and the two channel sections caused ripples in the plate between rivets which were placed at 6 inch centers. The cover plate, accounting for about half the area of the compression chord, because of the initaal deformations had lost most of its capacity to sustain compressive forces and therefore was ineffective to sustain almost any load. This is the reason for current stitch rivet requirements.

The capacity of a cover plate with an initial deformation Δ, midway between the rivet lines can be approximately determined by the following method.

4.2.3 Load Carrying Capacity of a Deformed Cover Plate

The critical buckling load of a pin ended column, with or without an initial deformation, shown in Figure 11, is given by:

$$P_{cr} = \frac{\pi^2 EI}{l^2} \qquad (1)$$

If the initial deformation of the coverplate, instead of being localized, as usually is the case, is uniform across the plate width, its buckling load could be obtained by the above equation. However, for plates of realistic dimensions the critical buckling stresses are much higher than the yield stress of steel and hence the yielding of a plate, rather than its instability, determines its load carrying capacity.

The eccentrically applied axial force P, which will cause complete yielding of a rectangular cross-section of width b and thickness t is given by:

$$P = P_p \left[\left(\frac{e}{2}\frac{P_p}{M_p}\right)^2 + 1\right]^{0.5} - \frac{e}{2}\frac{P_p^2}{M_p} \qquad (2)$$

where,

e = eccentricity of the applied load with respect to the centre of the cross section

P_p = plastic axial force capacity of the section

$= f_y bt$

M_p = plastic moment capacity of the section;

$= f_y \frac{bt^2}{4}$

When the coverplates of built up sections are deformed due to the accumulation of ruse between the plates and the parent sections, the deformation is usually limited to portions immediately above the parent sections. A portion of the plate between the parent sections, as shown in Figure 12 usually remains straight. To facilitate the calculation of its load carrying capacity, a deformed coverplate can be divided into three parts as shown in Figure 12. The load carrying capacity of parts A and C can be calculated by using the measured eccentricities from Equation (2). The neglect of the increase in actual eccentricities due to the presence of live load axial forces, as it is implied in Equation (2), can be approxiamtely compensated in determination of the load carrying capacity of part B of the plate (see Figure 12) as follows:

(1) Determine the increase of eccentricity Δ_A for plates A from the following equation:

$$\Delta_A = e_A \frac{\frac{P_A}{EI} \frac{l^2}{\pi^2}}{1 - \frac{P_A}{EI} \frac{l^2}{\pi^2}} \qquad (3)$$

where e_A is the measured eccentricity of plate A, P_A is the axial load calculated by equation (2) less the dead load axial force in A and l is equal to half the distance between rivets or bolts.

(2) Similarly obtain Δ_C for plate C.

(3) Calculate P for plate B by Equation (2), assuming $e = 0.5\ (\Delta_A + \Delta_C)$

The total capacity of the coverplate is then taken as the sum of the capacities of its three parts.

4.3 Connections

The determination of the load capacity of connections in a truss is difficult because they are not accessable for examination. A study of several trusses (47) in which the truss was dismantled has indicated that the pins in the eye bars lost approximately 25% of their material. Also, the eye bars had a reduced area of 40%. This reduction was due to wearing and rust.

In addition to pin connections, riveted elements need to be examined and rated. Estimates relative to the degree of material loss, reduction in allowable stress, and loading history must all be considered in the rating of the elements.

4.4 Fatigue

Fatigue in the structures under consideration is generally considered as the slow growth of small cracks under cyclic loading. Eventuallly the crack may become large enough to precipitate failure of the member. This failure will either occur in a ductile manner if the section is reduced sufficiently to permit the member to yield, or if the material is not tough enough at the temperature and loading rate considered, brittle fracture may occur.

<u>Loading Rates & Toughness</u>

For truss bridges loading rates are intermediate to slow as opposed to dynamic so that Charpy tests underestimate the service toughness of the material. Barsom gives the following formula for estimating dynamic fracture toughness values from Charpy tests.

$$\frac{(K_{1d})^2}{E} = 5\ \text{CVN} \qquad (4)$$

There is then a temperature shift of at least 70°F. to arrive at the Fracture Toughness for intermediate loading in most mild steels.

As an example, if a set of Charpy Tests give 15 foot-lbs. at 70°F then the dynamic fracture toughness is 47 ksi-½ inch at 70°F. and the intermediate loading rate fracture toughness is also 47 ksi-½ inch at 0°F.

Since most of the steels used for the truss bridges under consideration have transition temperatures above ambient the temperature shift is crucial.

There is a need at this point in time (1978) for similar information on wrought iron.

Given the appropriate fracture toughness, critical crack sizes can be derived for various defects. A fracture control plan can then be instituted to prevent catastrophic failure. This will be done either by inspection of the structure for cracks at suitable intervals, or by load restrictions that prevent critical crack sizes from developing, or a combination of the two.

In some cases, critical crack sizes are too small to be realistically discovered by inspection, and load restrictions to prevent serious crack growth during the remaining bridge life will be necessary.

Evaluation

The first consideration in evaluating a structure must be to avoid instability such as buckling, crushing, unstable crack growth or aerodynamic instability. In other words, to avoid failure under the one-of-a-kind loading. The second concerns obtaining the maximum service life. Obviously, one can live with higher loadings if reduced life is acceptable. In the ultimate bridge, ratings should be a function of the traffic to be carried.

The first attempt at rating for fatigue should be based on a crude national conservative traffic model. If the bridge proves adequate for this, then there is no need to check further.

If not, a more sophisticated check is required. The more valuable the structure, the more detailed the check can be.

The only people who can arrange to provide adequate loading information are the Governments involved, or in the case of railways, the railroads themselves.

This information must be obtained if anything but the crudest check is to be made. Some stab at past traffic may be required, otherwise some very conservative assumptions with regard to fatigue will be required.

Recommended Initial Procedures

Current rating procedures (1978) give little guidance on the assessment of bridges for fatigue. AASHTO and AREA have just commenced formulating a policy in this regard. In the interval, the following is recommended:

1. The details of the truss should be classified as to detail type according to the fatigue detail category given in the current AASHTO or AREA specifications (6). For example, a rivet hole is a "D" detail.
2. The stress range based on the current code design loading should be calculated.
3. The detail should be checked against current code design limits. For highway bridges this is a function of the current average daily truck traffic and the type of member. For railways it is solely a function of the span length and type of member.

Example

As an example consider a hanger of a typical truss. Suppose the worst detail at the location of highest stress is a group of rivets. The detail is then a Category "D" (1978). Assume that the stress range under the current code design loading is 16 ksi.

For the case of a highway structure assume the structure is on a major city street with more than 2500 trucks per day. AASHTO then requires that this member be checked for the two million cycle group. Although not mentioned above the member is part of a redundant load path structure. The permissible stress range is 10 ksi. By this check the members are not adequate. AASHTO also requires a check with a single lane loaded with the design truck for over two million cycles in which case the permissible stress range is 7 ksi, and for the lane loading for the 100000 group in which case the permissible stress range is 27 ksi. The last two were not considered in this example.

For the case of a railway structure assume the bridge is a single track bridge with 25 foot stringers. AREA requires that hangers be checked for the greater than two million category. The permissible stress range is 7 ksi. Again the member is not adequate.

The above is a crude assessment based on a conservative traffic model, and will give a quick but adequate check for many members. Unfortunately, not adequate for the example.

Further Checking

Members that fail the above test may still be adequate depending on their quality of fabrication, current condition and the actual past and projected load spectra. There is an example of a detailed check of a railway bridge in the literature (39, 40).

Consequences of Failure

For members that do fail the above analytical check, what is the consequence of failure? Is it htat important? Will it lead to collapse? Is the member or structure sufficiently redundant that collapse will not occur before the failure is easily detected (41)?

In order to properly rate a bridge one must understand the nature of the actual loading to which the bridge is to be subjected, and the actual strain behavior of the structure. It is very important to change ones basic thought pattern from thinking in terms of stress to visualizing deformations or strains.

As one part of a member fails, will it shed load elsewhere? Are the other members strong enough to carry this redistributed load long enough for routine inspection to discover the local failure and then to initiate corrective action?

In a built up section if one component cracks, will the rest of the section adequately carry the load for a sufficient interval? What are the chances of two or more parts of a built up section cracking together? For the bottom flange of a stringer made of two angles the probability is very small (4). This internal member redundancy (41) will enable many structures to carry loads which the current design methods cannot allow.

This principle of internal member redundancy does not apply if any welding has been done to the member, even tack welds. The inherent crack stopper (41) between component parts of a riveted built-up section is by-passed by the weld. A crack in one part of a member can then transfer to another part through the weld. This is particularly dangerous on old trusses as field welds tend to be of poorer quality than assumed by current codes.

Be very careful of any welding done to an old truss. It will almost certainly be a crack starter.

Accurate Stresses

Should the member not be sufficiently internally redundant, or should the other members of the truss not be able to adequately share the load, and assuming the member failed the first test, then an even more sophisticated check may be in order. The more valuable the structure, the more detailed the check.

In assessing the potential failure of a member in fatigue, the critical variables are stress and current flaw size. The flaw size varies as the three halves power, whereas stress varies to the cube with fatigue crack growth in mild steels. In wrought iron stress probably varies as the 4th or 5th power as opposed to the cube.

It is thus readily apparent that a small change in stress range will mean a significant improvement in life. Field measurements will probably indicate that the actual stresses are lower than the calculated valures (40, 42, 43) but not always. The ASCE Guide to the Field Testing of Bridges (43) should be of assistance.

If this is not sufficient, as assessment of past and projected loads must be made to establish actual load spectra (41, 47, 48). Care should be taken not to spend more on analysis either analytically or by field measurements than either adequate strengthening or replacement would cost (46).

5. FIELD TEST RATING EVALUATION

5.1 Behavior Test

5.1.1 General

In the past the engineer has relied on analytical procedures to determine the load capacity or rating of a truss bridge and have rarely used a field load test to rate the bridges, and even non-destructive tests of the components are not common because of the high costs. Visual inspection combined with computer analysis is typical. While AASHTO (9) permits a stress of 75% of F_y as the maximum allowable unit stress, many state engineers use 50% or 55% F_y as the maximum to offset the inaccuracies of inspection. The consensus is that well trained inspectors are the best means to rate old truss bridges. Inherently, the posting of such a structure requires the engineer to make rational and safe assumptions, in order to insure the integrity of the bridge and safety to the public. In order to insure such an analysis is adequate and to provide additional data, the bridge could be examined experimentally when subjected to actual design loadings. Such tests will then indicate the true response of the critical members, when subjected to induced live loading. This information can then be related to the analytical data and then judgements in the bridge ratings made.

5.1.2 Bridge Field Tests

In order to demonstrate the usefulness of conducting field tests on trusses, the results of such tests (47, 51, 52, 53, 54, 55, 56) will now be given. These tests were conducted on six truss bridges located in Frederick County, Maryland (47) and two trusses in Boone and Dales Counties in Iowa (5, 48).

(1) Maryland Bridges

The six truss bridges (51,52,53,54,55,56) that were field tested consist of single lane steel pinned jointed pony truss structures approximately 15.0' wide and spans of 60' to 90' long. With the exception of Gapland Road Bridge, the other five bridges have wooden decks. These decks are nailed to nailing strips which are attached to the steel stringers. The deck members are generally wooden 3" x 10" and the nailers are wooden 3" x 10" either of pine or oak. The Gapland Road Bridge deck consists of a steel grating.

Each of the six bridges was instrumented with SR-4 strain gages at various positions. It should be noted that for heavily loaded trusses (Rail Loading) and uncertainties in the structure a minimum of four gages should be employed to insure correct assessment of the axial loaded members. For these bridges, generally one/two gages were used for the axial members, the location of which will now be described:

a) Long Mill Road Bridge (51)

Seven strain gages were attached to this bridge, as shown in Figure 13. One gage each was attached to the two main bottom chords, one gage on the floor beam, and a gage on each of two stringers. One stringer has a nailing strip and one does not. The gages are located at midspan of each member.

b) Daysville Road Bridge (52)

Six strain gages were attached to this bridge, as shown in Figure 14. Two gages were attached to the top chord of the truss, one gage on the vertical, one gage on the bottom horizontal, one gage on the floor beam, and one on the stringer. All gages were attached at midspan of the members except the vertical and bottom horizontal. At these positions, the gages were attached near the pin of the truss.

c) Water Street Bridge (53)

Six strain gages were also attached to this bridge, as shown in Figure 15. One gage was attached to the top chord, one gage on each of the two main diagonals, one gage on the bottom chord, and one gage on the stringer floor beam. All gages were attached at midspan of all members.

d) Crum Road Bridge (54)

Seven strain gages were attached to this structure, as shown in Figure 16. One gage each was attached to the center and end of the top chords, one gage on the end and center bottom chords, one gage on the end vertical, and a gage on the floor beam and stringer. All gages were attached at midspan of each member.

e) Gapland Road Bridge (55)

Seven strain gages were attached to this structure, as shown in Figure 7. Two gages were attached to the end vertical, one gage on a diagonal, one gage on a bottom horizontal, a gage on a stringer and floor beam, and one gage on a "U" bolt, which is attached to the fllor beam and pin joint. The gage on the end vertical and bottom horizontal are attached at the end of the member, adjacent to the pin. All other gages are attached at midspan of the members.

f) Old Hagerstown Road Bridge (56)

Six strain gages were attached to this bridge, as shown in Figure 18. One gage was attached to a diagonal, one placed on the bottom chord (Fig. 19) one on each of three stringers, and one on a floor beam. Each was attached at the center of each member.

Loading

The truck load that was applied to each bridge consisted of a gravel loaded 2D truck (Fig. 20). The rear axle weight is of the order of 22.5 kps, which was positioned along the bridge at various locations, as dictated by the influence lines, to institute maximum effects. These trucks are similar to the design H-15 vehicle, which has a rear axle weight of 24^K and front axle weight of 6^K. This type of vehicle represents the worst possible load to which each bridge might be susceptible.

Test Results

The truck described in Table 3 was placed on each truss bridge at various positions, and the induced strains on the various members recorded. In some instances, the strain gages were monitored for both static and dynamic loading, the results of which are given in Ref. (47).

(2) Iowa Bridges

The two bridges that were field tested were the Hubby Bridge in Boone County and the Chestnut Ford Bridge in Dallas County. Both of the bridges consisted of wrought iron pinned-jointed trusses with steel floor beams and timber decks.

The Hubby Bridge consisted of four modified Parker type high truss simple spans (Fig. 21, 22) each 165 ft. long. The trusses consisted of tension eyebars of both square and rectangular cross sections, built-up laced channels for the end posts and upper chord compression members, and laced channels for the other compression members. The deck (Fig. 23) was built of timber stringers, timber cross beams, and timber floor planks.

The Chestnut Ford Bridge (Figs. 24, 25) was compost of four high truss simple spans. Three of the spans were modified Pratt-type trusses each 150 ft. long, with the fourth span being a Pratt truss 180 ft. long. Only one of the 150 ft. spans was tested.

The test truss consisted of tension eyebars of circular, square or rectangular cross sections for tension members, of built-up laced channels for end posts and upper chord compression members and of laced channels for the remaining compression members.

The deck (Fig. 26) was built-up of timber stringers and timber floor planks. The cross planks were placed on edge on top of the stringers and laminated together with bolts and were spiked to the stringers.

Each of the test spans was instrumented with electric resistance strain gages. The two test spans of the Hubby Bridge were instrumented with over 100 gages as shown in Fig. 27. Several typical members, including verticals, diagonals and main tension members, were instrumented.

Loading

The truck load that was applied to each bridge (Fig. 28) consisted of a standard gravel loaded dump truck. The rear axle weights were about 22,000 lbs. with the front axle weighing about 4,000 lbs. The trucks were positioned along the bridges at various panel points, both in concentric and eccentric positions, to maximize the stresses in various members.

Test Results

The stresses (and forces) computed from the measured strains were compared with those obtained from theoretical analysis of the trusses. The truss was assumed to be poinned at each joint although it was realized that considerable restraint may be realized at the joints from rust, etc. Typical results are shown in Fig. 29.

The results show the relationship between the total member force and the position of the rear axle of the loaded truck. The results shown are for a concentric loading on the Hubby Bridge. It can be seen that the results from the field tests compare very favorably with those from the analysis. Thus, it appears that the use of a simplified pinned-joint analysis is appropriate for these types of trusses.

5.1.3 Bridge Design Study

Bridge Rating

As mentioned previously, each of the six Maryland bridges have been rated, as based on a complete analytical study (51,52,53,54,55,56). The resulting ratings were obtained after computing the probably induced dead and live load stresses and the allowable stresses. The allowable stresses were selected from the AASHTO Specification in "Manual for Maintenance Inspection of Bridges" and field observations, i.e., a reduction in the design value of certain members was used if the member was noted to be distorted or corroded. With these criteria and field observations of the various members, the rating of each bridge was computed. The ratings correspond to H-15 truck with an appropriate reduction.

Those members which govern the rating of each bridge are as follows:

Long Mills Road	Stringers	Gages 4,5	HO
Crum Road	Floor Beam	Gage 2	H2
Water Street	Diagonal	Gage 1	H1.2
Daysville Road	Stringer, Floor Beam	Gages 1,5	H3
Old Hagerstown Rd.	Stringer	Gages 3,4,5	H1
Gapland Road	Diagonal	Gage 7	H5

Assuming the dead load stresses as computed are accurate, it remains to establish the occurance of the live load stresses. Such stresses have been obtained through tests discussed herein, thus using these field live load stresses in conjunction with the computed dead load stresses, the bridges can be re-rated.

The Iowa Hubby Bridge was inspected by maintenance forces of the Iowa Department of Transportation and the results provided to three of the cooperating agencies in the program (Iowa State University, U.S. Army Corps of Engineers, and Highway Division - Iowa Department of Transportation. Using the data from the inspection as a base, each agency computed the rating of the bridge using the AASHTO "Manual for Maintenance Inspection of Bridges" (10).

Ratings were requested for each of the three separate portions of the truss tested, i.e., the deck, the floorbeams, and the trusses. The results of the ratings are shown in the following Table.

Bridge Ratings (operating)

Bridge Portion	Agency		
	1	2	3
Deck	H 13.1	H 8.2	H 9.4
Floorbeam	H 2.4[a]	H 7.4	H 6.7
Truss	H 11.4	H 12.7	H 11.9

[a] Did not consider beam laterally supported
[b] Initial fracture of L_5M_5

It can be seen that the ratings are quite consistent for the truss. However, there is a variation in the ratings for the floor system. In the case of the floorbeams, the assumptions related to lateral support of the compression flange are critical. The table shows the effect of this assumption in the rating of the floorbeam.

Laboratory Study

Purpose of Tests

As described in the previous section 5.1.3, "Design Study", three out of the six Maryland bridges have ratings which are governed by the strength of the stringers. In most instances, these low ratings are due to the conditions that no lateral bracing of the compression flange is assumed. In order to rectify this condition, the Frederick County Engineer has devised a method of providing continuous lateral bracing by attaching wooden 3" x 8" nailing strips to each stringer. The top deck is then nailed to the nailing strips, thus providing continuous lateral support.

In order to determine the effectiveness of this type of bracing, a series of laboratory tests were conducted. It was the purpose of these tests to accurately evaluate the strength of the stringer members and thus provide an alternative rating.

Model Descriptions

Two models were constructed for test purposes. One model consisted of three 6112.7, 10.0' long steel girders, spaced at 3.0 feet. The three girders were welded at each end to 3" x 3" steel angles. The other model consisted of the same members, but had nailing strips bolted to the side of each stringer. Attached to each strip were 3" x 10" wooden planks.

Each model was instrumented with SR-4 strain gages attached on the top and bottom flanges at midspan. Vertical deformation at midspan of the models was also measured during each test.

The models were subjected to two loads applied on the top flange of the center girder. The model which did not have nailing strips did have similar planking laid across the model width.

Material Properties

Sample coupon specimens from each test model were tested to determine the material properties. The results from these tests are summarized below:

Test Coupon	F_y(ksi)	F_u(ksi)
1	38.8	63.8
2	39.6	52.5
3	36.7	58.0
4	38.7	63.8
Average	38.4	59.5

The modulus of elasticity of two of these specimens was also obtained giving an average value of $E = 30.0 \times 10^3$ ksi. This value of E was used in converting all field strain data to stresses.

A summary of the induced girder stresses is also given in Table 4. It should be noted that the maximum stress prior to excessive distortion or buckling of the member was 24.0 ksi of the model without nailers. However, when nailers were added, it was possible to increase the load capacity until yielding of the girder was instituted, as given in Table 4

These can be further examined by computing the percent distribution of the total stress in each girder. The model without nailers gives an average distribution of the stress on load 14% - 72% - 14% to the end-center-end girder. The model with nailers gave an average distribution of 22% - 56% - 22% load. These results give a distribution factor of S/4.2 and S/5.4 for the deck without and with nailers, respectively. Thus, the advantage of nailing strips is evident from the increase in the load distribution.

Examination of the AASHTO code suggests that the distribution factor for a fraction of wheel load to a stringer which has a plank floor is S/4.0. This agrees with the tests on the beams without nailers; however, when nailers are used, the distribution factor is S/5.4 or an increase of 20%.

5.2 Ultimate Load Test

As part of the overall study of the behavior of the high-truss Hubby Bridge in Boone County, Iowa (48, 49) ultimate load tests were conducted on the truss system, the timber floor and the floorbeams (11, 50).

As noted earlier the Hubby Bridge is a four span simply supported pin - connected single lane high truss with a timber stringer - plank floor supported on steel I-beam stringers. The purpose of the tests was to determine the ultimate capacity of each basic component and compare that with the rated operating capacity.

The ultimate load test of the timber floor consisted of two parts. The first part was typical of a truck proceeding along the roadway centerline (Figs. 30, 31) while the second part (Figs. 32, 33) were similar except that the load was in the most eccentric condition.

The floorbeams of the bridge were used as the reactions for the testing system used (Figs. 31, 33, 34). The self-contained system was capable of applying a simulated rear axle load. Because of capacity problems with the system, the axle load was applied as a dual load rather than a single load.

The test showed the significant effect of the transverse distribution planks in distributing the load to a member of stringers. The capacity of the deck was controlled by the eccentric load case where failure occurred at a level equivalent to a H32 truck, which, as would be expected, is considerably above the operating rating. The center loading failure occurred at a level equivalent to a H42 truck.

Probably, the most significant ultimate load tests were the ones on two of the floorbeams. The purposes of these tests were to determine the actual capacity of the beams and to indicate the actual lateral support of the beams in contrast to that normally assumed. As noted in Section 5.1, the rating of the floorbeam was markedly affected by the assumed lateral support condition.

The loading system is shown in Fig. 35. Two jacks were used and placed at 6 ft. spacing directly over the beam to simulate the heavy rear truck axle. The effects of the front axle was neglected.

Typical results of the tests are shown in Fig. 36. It shows the load-deflection curves for 5 transverse positions on the beam for one of the two floorbeams tested. Three observations should be noted. First, the actual behavior fell between the two extreme assumed end conditions, i.e., fixed or pinned ends. The end connections were framed riveted angles connected to channels through which the pins of the truss joint passed.

Second, the load-deflection curve was linear nearly up to ultimate load with a marked increase in deflection near ultimate load. The increase started when lateral support was lost. This support was provided simply by the timber stringers pressing on the top flange of the floorbeam. It should be noted that some dapping of the timber had occurred.

Third, the ultimate capacity was equivalent to a load produced by a H30 truck. It was considerably higher than the operating rating and shows the importance of actually determining lateral support conditions at service loads for rating purposes. If lateral support is not available, consideration should be given to providing some as it significantly increases the rating.

The major phase of the ultimate load test program was the testing of the truss system. The data recording system included strain gages on many critical members and truss deflection installations. The loads were applied to the center panel points (Fig. 37 in a 4 to 1 ratio to simulate a loaded truck through a dead weight system (Fig. 38).

The critical member determined from the analysis was L_5M_5 (center vertical) where the heavy rear axle would be placed. Figure 39 shows the vertical deflection of the center of the truss (L_5) and Fig. 40 shows the force in the critical member in comparison to the total load on the truss. Failure of member L_5M_5 occurred in the forging of the end eye for the pinned joint to the square bar used as the main member. This failure resulted in the marked increase in centerline deflection.

The loading of the truss at the initial failure of the critical member was equivalent to a H66.5 truck. However, the truss was capable of carrying a substanially higher load.

In summary, the ultimate load tests of the timber floor deck, floor-beams and the truss showed that the following system was by far, the most critical. The ultimate capacity of all parts of the system was considerably above the operating rating of each part. This is demonstrated in the following:

Bridge ratings (operating and test).

Bridge Portion	Agency Ratings (Table A)	Test Capacity (Rating)
Deck	H8.2-H13.1	H32
Floorbeam	H2.4-H7.4	H30
Truss	H11.4-H12.7	H66.5

6. ANALYSIS DATA FOR RATING

6.1 Properties

Since the rating of a span requires determination of the residual strength of the individual members available for live loads and impact after deducting requirements for dead load and other unavoidable loads from the member capacity, accurate estimates of member capacity are required. These estimates will provide both a guide for load limitation and identification of those members that should be strengthened to improve span capacity. Members capacity is dependent on member geometry and material properties.

The investigation of member geometry involves both the determination of the intended dimensions of all members, including material added for repairs or strengthening, which is required for estimating dead load and gives an upper bound for member capacity, and the determination of accidental variations in geometry, including reduction in section due to cracks, corrosion or added holes and curvature in compression members, which will reduce the capacity of the member.

The amount of expense justified for obtaining material information depends on the practical difference between a rating based on conservative assumptions regarding material properties and a rating based on improved knowledge of the material. A material determination or assumption must be made for each member as mixing steel and wrought iron members in the same span or using high strength steel for highly stressed members with mild steel for less highly stressed members has been a frequent practice. The distinction of steel from wrought iron by examining filed or ground surfaces for slag inclusions or by spark testing are discussed in reference (4). Hardness tests indicate the strength of steel. If the actual strength of the material is to be used instead of published conservative values based on material identification, minimum properties must be determined from fabrication records or test coupons obtained from critical members. Test coupons should be taken from locations that will not affect the strength or durability of the member or appropriate repairs must be made. If coupons are to be removed by flame cutting, the possible effect of heat on the material involved should be considered.

6.2 Floor Systems

Since floor systems are composed of flexural members, both the section loss and the location at which the loss occurs affect the member strength. A system to reduce the quantity of data supplied for bending strength analyses of simple spans without significantly affecting the quality of the analysis follows:

For a member with uniform section throughout its length, report the minimum remaining section in the center half of the member and its location. Report reduced sections in the end quarters of the member only if they are less than the minimum section in the center half.

For cover plated members, divide the member into inner and outer zones, "A and B" zones, respectively, in Figure 41 with the inner zones consisting of the zone included by the center half of the shortest cover plate and the pairs of zones included between the end of one cover plate and a section half-way to the end of the next longer cover plate. Report the minimum section in the inner zone or pair of inner zones for each change in section. Report the minimum section in an outer zone only if it is less than the minimum section in the corresponding inner zone. If the minimum section in each zone is assumed to exist at the section for maximum movement within the zone, the top chords and web members or 5(width/length) in bottom of thru trusses at hangers.

6.3 Trusses

Unless secondary stresses are large, it is practical to assume that the minimum section of a truss member is the critical section regardless of its location. Bent compression members will present a particular problem in analysis as there have been many inconsistancies observed in the behavior of spans with this type of damage. If the cost of repairing the bent members cannot be readily justified, proof testing to verify capacity may be appropriate.

Although modern truss designs typically avoid ambiguity regarding member behavior, many older, pin-connected trusses with apparently redundant members are statically determinate. Since eye bars will buckle under very small compressive loads, panels with eye bar diagonals and counters should be analyzed by neglecting the compressed member. A Whipple truss should be analyzed as a system of two Pratt trusses, one with diagonals ending at the even numbered lower panel points and the other with diagonals ending at the odd numbered lower panel points. The stresses in chord members and end posts are given by the stresses from the two analyses added together.

In the case of the Whipple truss, there is no physical connection between the members in the web systems except at the tops of the end posts and the consideration of the two web systems as independent is correct. In the case of other trusses with multiple web systems, the web members in the two systems are connected to each other and the approximation of independent systems should not be used now that computer programs capable of analyzing the entire truss as a plane frame are available.

6.4 Computer Programs

A computer program for rating railway truss bridges in accordance with the 1967 A.R.E.A. specifications is available through the Association of

American Railroads Research Center. The output consists of the Cooper rating for each truss member. The more important limitations of the program include a maximum span length of 620 feet (189. meters) and a requirement that the truss contain no more than 25 panels, 50 joints, or 100 members. The number and arrangement of panels with counters and the maximum slenderness ratio of compression members are limited. The program can be used for continuous or internally indeterminate trusses.

As in all computer programs, input data must be properly coded if valid results are to be obtained. Input data include data to define the truss geometry, area and section modulus of members, type of steel in members, locations and directions of reactions, dead load panel point loads, impact data and data required to define the distribution of loads between trusses of double track spans.

The following listed computer programs are those which have been most frequently utilized for bridge rating and analysis.

Associated with these programs are various details and capabilities. Table 5 gives the program description, computer machine utilized and languages for each program. Table 6 gives the bridge types analyzed, construction material and general capabilities. Table 7 gives the analysis capabilities and Table 8 the automatic capabilities.

6.4.1 Program Details

(1) Bridge Rating and Analysis Structural System (BRASS)
(2) A Computer System for Analyzing and Rating Bridges
(3) Bridge Analysis and Rating (BRRAT)
(4) Overload Route System (OVLOAD)

The descriptions for these programs follow.

(1) Bridge Rating and Analysis Structural System (BRASS)

Categories: Bridge Rating; Highway Bridge Design; Highway Bridge Review; Bridge Engineering Computer Programs.

Title: Bridge Rating and Analysis Structural System (BRASS)

Authors: Ralph R. Johnston; Robert H. Day and Dan A. Glandt; Wyoming Highway Department; P.O. 1708, Cheyenne, Wyoming, 82001.

Maintenance: Authors.

Date: September 1973.

Capability: System includes bridge design, structural inventory, deck design and review, structural analysis, structural loading, and girder section design and review. The types of structure are divided into six groups. The groups include: cell type layout, continuous beam bridge, rigid frame, slant leg structure, and rigid frame box culverts. The system is capable of analyzing reinforced concrete, structural steel and timber.

Method: The method of analysis for beam is column analogy. The method used in the analysis for cell structure or slant leg rigid frame is slope-deflection method. Gauss-Jordan inversion is used to invert the matrix, virtual work method is applied to calculate deflection.

Limit: The system only considers working stress method. It cannot analyze hinge and cantilever structure and at least one truck wheel has to be applied at the structure.

Programming Language: FORTRAN

Documentation: Complete and current

Input: The system consists of design review and load rating subsystem. The executive control has the duty of determining the next job.

The input cards, called control cards, are followed by data cards which determine the phases to follow in a given component.

Output: The output consists of verification of input data, design reports and rating reports. The first report is always printed, but the last two are printed only if requested. The user may control over output desired. That is, by coding, he could obtain intermediate output, along with final results.

Software: Operating: Batch.

Hardware: The programs are coded on the IBM 360/40. Utilizing a storage capacity of 72K bytes. May be run on most 3rd generation computers.

Usage: The system is developed by the Wyoming Highway Department and used by several state agencies.

Typical Running Time:

Availability through Wyoming Highway Department or U.S. Department of Transportation - FHWA.

(2) A Computer System for Analyzing and Rating Bridges

Categories: Bridge Analysis; Rating; Girders; Truss; Live Load.

Title: A Computer System for Analyzing and Rating Bridges (BARS)

Authors: Control Data Corporation, P.O. Box 1980, Twin Cities Airport Station, MN 55111.

Maintenance: Authors.

Date: Spring 1972.

Capability: The system can perform the inventory rating, operatingrating, posting rating and special permit analysis. It can analyze five member types which are decking, stringer, floor beam, girder and trusses. Construction materials may be one of the following: structural steel, reinforced concrete, composite steel, prestress concrete, composite prestress concrete.

Method:

Limitations: Only allowable stress method is considered here. Live loads are limited to five truck types.

Programming language: FORTRAN

Documentation: Complete and current.

Input: The input consists of the geometries, properties of members, materials, and load data. System is production oriented and designed to batch process bridges of the same type. The first sheet summarizes the results while additional sheets provide detailed information.

Output: The first sheet for a bridge provides summary information indicating the rating of the bridge. Following the summary sheet are data sheets for each member rated providing the detail that supports the rating for that member. In addition to that, a tape file is written that will retain the data for the bridge that will be needed for insurance of special permits or for future ratings due to increased legal load limits.

Software Operating: Batch or RJE to CDC 6600. Batch or O.S. to IBM 360/50.

Hardware: The system is programmed for an IBM 360/50 having 512K primary storage.

Usage: The system is developed for Illinois Division of Highways and used by several other state agencies.

Typical running time:

Availability: Via service station of Control Data Corporation.

(3) Bridge Analysis and Rating (BRRAT)

Categories: Bridge rating; Live Load; Rating Factor; Girder; Floor Beam; Stringer; Truss.

Title: Bridge Analysis and Rating (BRRAT)

Authors: Pennsylvania Department of Transportation.

Maintenance: Authors.

Date:

Capability: Program calculate Inventory, Operating and Safe Load Capacity Ratings for single span concrete slab or T-beam bridges, multigirder composite or noncomposite bridges, girder-floor beam-stringer system or truss-floorbeam-stringer system. Ratings are computed for H20, HS20, ML70, Type 3S2 and Type 3-3 loadings and may be requested for maximum of 24 axles.

Method: The method of analysis is matrix method and Gauss-Jordan inversion.

Limit: The ratings are limited to working stress method. Not able to analyze cantilever structures.

Programming Language: FORTRAN

Documentation: Complete and current.

Input: The data to be entered depends on the type of bridge to be analyzed. Input consists of Multigirder system (GGG), Girder-Floor beam-Stringer System (GFS), Truss-Floorbeam-Stringer System (TFS) and Concrete Slab or T-Beam Bridge.

Output: The output also printed out according to above four categories to have inventory, operating and safe load capacity rating factors in a fixed form.

Software Operating: Batch or remote.

Hardware:

Usage: The system is developed by Penn. Department of Transportation.

Typical Running Time:

Availability: via Pennsylvania Department of Transportation.

(4) Overload Route System (OVLOAD)

Categories: Bridge Rating; Highway Route; Overload; Live Load.

Title: Overload Route System (OVLOAD).

Authors: Kenneth R. White, John Minor, Department of Civil Engineering, New Mexico State University, Box 3CE, Las Cruces, NM 88003.

Maintenance: Authors and New Mexico State Highway Department.

Date: 12 September 1974.

Capability: The program OVLOAD can be used to check a proposed routing of a giving overload (truck or object) requiring an overload permit) within the State of New Mexico utilizing the data bank created by the bridge inspectors of the New Mexico State Highway Department.

Method: Matrix stiffness method is used where one span as one member.

Limitation: Working stress method is applied here. No variation of member, hinge or cantilever structures are considered. No member or shear influence lines are constructed where only critical point is given.

Programming language: FORTRAN

Input: OVLOAD is operational on the CMS terminals connected to the NMSHD IBM 370. The bridge data which was accumulated with the NMSHD Bridge Inventory System is stored on disk within the CMS system. The data bank is periodically updated by the ECU from the master file: The program OVLOAD is accessed and used by the executive program OVERLOAD which sets up the necessary files for execution.

Output: Page one is a listing of all input data. Succeeding pages list the output data which are lists of all inadequate bridges.

Software Operating: CMS terminal to IBM 360/55.

Hardware: IBM 360/55, tape reader, teleprocessing unit having 126K core.

Usage: OVLOAD was developed as a joint project between the New Mexico State Highway Department and

Typical Running Time:

Availability: New Mexico State Highway Department.

7. PROCEDURES FOR IMPROVING BRIDGE BEHAVIOR

7.1 Strengthening

The following is based on the outline given in the AREA Manual (57) as modified by CN Rail (58).

7.1.1 General

"The strengthening of existing bridges is usually occasioned by the necessity for carrying heavier live loads than those for which they were designed. It may also be required because of inadequate design (usually in the proportioning of details) or as the result of localized deterioration." (57)

The decision as to whether a bridge is to be strengthened or replaced should take into account potential traffic and future use, the condition of the structure, the metal of which the various members are made, the fatigue effect of the live loads that have been operated over the structure, the potential for catastropic collapse, the comparative estimated costs, the added length of life to be obtained for the strengthened bridge and the possible future increase in the live load.

For certain relatively high required rates of return, it is economical to spend up to 80% of the replacement cost of a structure on strengthening. As public funds become more scarce, the incidence of such strengthening must increase. This is in addition to structures that are to be preserved for historical or aesthetic reasons.

Generally, strengthening should aim at raising the capacity of a bridge of low rating to the equivalent strength of all or most bridges on the route taking into account real future loads. If the sole source of heavy traffic is the occasional school bus, strengthening to HS 20 may not be necessary even if adjacent structures are that strong.

The strengthening should increase the rating of the weak parts to the existing strength of the parts that require no strengthening, if this is feasible and economical.

If enforcement of load limits, etc. is possible, then strengthening to permit loads at restricted speed (i.e.: reduced impact) or under certain controllable climatic conditions (say half wind or warm weather only) may be justified. Railroads have a better chance of doing this.

In deciding the level of strengthening required, remember that certain code loadings and distributions are somewhat arbitary. For example, the AASHTO distribution factors (59) or the AREA (60) wind and nosing requirements. The wind loading (61) was initially established by calculation as the horizontal force required to blow over an 1890 type railway car on the theory that trains would not operate under more severe conditions.

The nosing (62) requirement was initially established to ensure that there would be at least 3 rivets in lateral connections.

Although wind loads are expected to be lower than the code, the hunting of empty railway cars can produce forces higher than the current nosing force.

These two lateral forces, together wiht the 2-1/2% of main member forces, have served the North American Railway Community well. It would be prudent not to reduce the total resultant force and load combination factors without sufficient experimental and theoretical justification. Obviously, the same principle applies to highway bridges.

Work interrupting the flow of traffic should be avoided or kept to a minimum in planning the strengthening. Any required traffic restriction during some phases of the strengthening should be noted on the strengthening plans.

7.1.1.1 Physical Condition

The physical condition of the structure must be determined by a detailed inspection. Corroded parts should be replaced or strengthened to original strength unless calculations or tests prove this is not necessary.

The kind of metal of which the various components are made should be determined, together with their physical and chemical properties. Usually this may be determined by examining the original drawings, specifications or test records. In some cases, it may be necessary to obtain specimens of the metal from various components. References (61, 63, 64) give some guidance on typical metal bridge materials.

7.1.1.2 Details

Generally, connections determine whether truss strengthening is even economically possible.

When strengthening any part of a bridge, poor details should be rectified, even if they have no measurable influence on the rating.

7.1.1.3 Stresses

As nearly as possible, Waddell's Principle XLII (62) should be followed:

"There is but one correct method of checking thoroughly the entire detailing of a finished design for a structure, viz:

'Follow each stress given on the stress diagram from its point of application on one main member until it is transferred completely to either other main members or to the substructure, and see that each plate, pin, rivet, or other detail by which it travels has sufficient strength in every particular to resist properly the stress that it thus carries; check also the sizes of such parts as stay-plates and lacing, which are not affected by the stresses given on the diagram, and see that said sizes are in conformity with the best modern practice.'"

The unit stresses permissible in the added material in strengthened members under the load for which they are strengthened should not exceed current accepted levels.

Unless the dead load stress is removed temporarily from the member or some means is provided to introduce the proper dead load stress in the new metal when it is applied, the new material should be considered as carrying the live load only. Connections of adequate strength are required for the added metal.

When the added metal carries the live load only, the stresses in the remaining proportion of the original member which is carrying the total dead load stress, should be investigated under the load for which the bridge is strengthened.

Any temporary reduction of the effective section of a member during strengthening such as the removal of rivets, cover plates, lacing bars, or other parts will permanently increase the dead load unit stresses.

If live load is permitted under these conditions, it must be checked.

If falsework or other means to prevent additional stresses are advisable, this must be noted on the strengthening drawing.

7.1.1.4 Compatibility

Particularly in the case of added components, the principle of consistent deformations must not be violated.

7.1.1.5 Eccentricity

The added metal should be applied so as to produce a balanced section, eliminating or minimizing the effect of eccentricity on the strengthened member. When a balanced section cannot be economically obtained, the eccentricity of the member must be taken into account in determining the resultant stresses.

7.1.1.6 Welding

Welding eliminates the inherent crack stoppers between component parts of riveted or bolted structures, reducing the safety factor against brittle fracture. This must be accounted for in choosing permissible fatigue stresses as is done in the current AASHTO specifications (65).

Welding also makes a structure more susceptible to distress due to displacement induced secondary stresses. These must be determined and their effects evaluated. Proper detailing becomes far more critical.

Field welding must meet current AWS criteria in order for code stress limits to be applicable. This is difficult and will require rigorous inspections.

When welds are added to existing riveted connections, the welds should be designed to transmit the entire stress, except that in members where the existing material carries the entire dead load stress, the welds may be designed to carry the entire live load stress in the member. Where some of the existing rivets in a member are loose or defective, high strength bolts properly installed may be used to carry the dead load stress, if they are installed before the welding.

7.1.2 Floor Systems

7.1.2.1 Stringers and Floor Beams

Most State Highway Administrations agree that the floor system is the weakest area of old truss bridges. Adding and replacing stringers and floor beams and welding flange plates to critical areas are used to strengthen floor systems. Kentucky and other states have found that placing new floor beams is most economical (Figure 42).

In order to minimize the dead weight of the floor system, steel-grid decking has been used to replace timber or concrete floors (69).

Stringer systems may be strengthened by adding cover plates to existing stringers, by adding additional stringers or by replacement with a new section of adequate strength. Wherever possible, additional or new stringers should be standard rolled sections without cover plates in preference to built-up sections. When additional stringers are used they should be connected to the existing stringers so that they will deflect together. The spacing of stringers should be such as to allow inspection, cleaning and painting of the interior surfaces. For further guidance, see Section 15-7-5 of the AREA Manual (60).

The webs of floorbeams are likely to be over-stressed at the ends, especially in pin-connected truss spans where the ends have been recessed to clear the pin-nuts and eyebars. This detail of the floorbeams should be analyzed for both flange and web stresses and adequate reinforcement provided.

7.1.2.2 Stiffeners

The bearing stiffeners may be reinforced by adding angles or plates, grinding the bearing ends of the new parts to make them fit closely, or welding them to the flanges.

Intermediate stiffeners may be added by riveting, high-strength bolting or welding, provided current code fatigue requirements are adhered to.

7.1.2.3 Diaphragms

Ineffective shallow diaphragms should be replaced with proper diaphragms which, in the case of multiple beams, will make them deflect together.

7.1.2.4 Flange Rivets

Where flange material is added, the flange riveting may be insufficient. This should be corrected by adding rivets or bolts, or substituting larger rivets or bolts.

7.1.2.5 Splices

If the web was not originally spliced to resist moment, it may be so spliced by adding cover plates or side plates.

7.1.2.6 Effective Span

If the bridge seat is wide, the effective span may be shortened somewhat by moving the bearings nearer to the edge of the seat and providing new end stiffener angles over them, if a thorough analysis of the abutments indicates that excessive soil pressure or pile loadings will not be obtained.

7.1.2.7 End Connections

The end connection of a stringer sometimes may be strengthened by using longer connecting angles and more rivets, by reaming the holes and using larger rivets, or by thoughtful welding. Also, brackets may be placed under the ends of the stringers to give additional support.

7.1.2.8 Lateral Bracing

Inadequate bracing systems, especially those composed of rods or bars, should be replaced with proper bracing of required strength and rigidity.

The lateral bracing between compression flanges or chords of deck spans sould resist 2-1/2% of the total axial compressive force at any section in addition to the lateral forces due to wind, centrifugal force and any other specified load.

7.1.2.9 Lateral Connections

Lateral plates attached to the tension flange of short-span stringers and floorbeams decrease their fatigue strength and the addition of such plates should be avoided, particularly near points of maximum bending.

7.1.2.10 Continuous Members

The capacity of interior stringers will be increased if the end connections are made continuous.

7.1.2.11 Substitution

Where extensive strengthening is to be done on a number of identical stringer spans, one new span may be provided and substituted for one of the spans which will then be removed and strengthened. Each span in turn will be replaced by a span that has been taken out and strengthened in this manner, until the entire bridge has been strengthened.

7.1.3 Trusses

The strengthening of trusses is more difficult and requires considerably more analysis of the connections and their details, than are required for the strengthening of floor systems. The connections often determine the strength of the span.

7.1.3.1 Tension Members

Tension members of pin-connected trusses often may be reinforced by the addition of adjustable bars. These may be of several types, such as loop bars or single bars attached to a loop or forging that fits over and bears on the pin. Care must be taken, however, to form the portion of the bar or forging in contact with the pin so that full bearing will be secured, preferably with an attachment bearing on one-half of the pin. This may be accomplished by providing excess metal in this portion and boring the pin holes. Where a bar of uniform section is bent around a pin, the cross section is likely to be reduced by the stretching of the bar and a narrowing of the outer edge, for which allowance shall be made. Where pin room is limited, bars sometimes are placed over the heads of existing eyebars, but this method gives doubtful results, because the edges of the eyebar heads are not finished to a true surface.

Except where a single bar can be placed in the exact center of the pin, two additional bars or members equally spaced from the center of the pin, should be used to strengthen each panel. The resultant stresses in the pins under the revised loading condition, must be investigated to insure the validity of the structure.

After the new members have been installed, the entire panel should be adjusted to properly distribute the dead load tension to all members. Eyebars or rods that do not have adjustable provisions, can be adjusted in accordance with Section 8.2 of Chapter 15 of the AREA Manual (60).

Elongated eyebars may be adjusted in accordance with the same Section 8.2.

Parts of corroded bars can be replaced by first detensioning with the aid of electrothermal flexible furnaces clamped on to each bar; the power for heating of the furnaces is by current from a standard portable welding generator. The expansion resulting from this heating will reduce the tensile stress to zero in 10-15 minutes with the temperature rising to a maximum of about 200°F. Mechanical dial strain gauges are used to record the reduction in stresses. When the new parts of each bar are fitted, the repaired member is post-tensioned by straining with high-tensile bars between two brackets temporarily bolted to the member on each side of the splice. Jacks are used to apply a force equivalent to the dead load stress to be transferred. Double butt straps or splice plates are drilled and bolted with high-strength bolts while the bars are held at the required stress (68).

Rolled or built-up sections may be effectively reinforced by the addition of cover plates in the planes of the gusset plates, riveted, high-strength bolted or welded to the flange of the member and butt welded to the gusset plates, providing the strength of the gusset plate and its connections is adequate. Care shall be taken to protect against notches or other severe stress concentrations and in satisfying code fatigue provisions at the connections of the cover plates to the gussets. Unless the dead load stress in the original member is relieved, new metal so added should be considered effective in carrying its portion of the live load stress only.

Floorbeam hangers are frequently highly stressed from a combination of bending and direct axial tension. To reduce the possibility of fatigue cracking in these highly stressed hangers, sharp copes or re-entrant cuts should be eliminated or modified. The use of high-strength bolts at the top connection of the floorbeam hangers to replace all rivets should also be considered to improve the load transfer to the gusset plates. In the case of odd-panel bridges, the middle panel will have cross diagonals, "counters". The variation from tension to compression causes relaxation in these counters. The addition of turnbuckles allows maintenance crews to keep a constant tension in the counters.

Virginia developed an end connection detail for pin joints which combines ease of member replacement with the capacity for tension adjustment (Figure 43).

7.1.3.2 Compression Members

The reinforcement of compression members requires careful investigation. The chord members of many old bridges are unsymmetrical in section and are eccentrically loaded. This condition may be corrected by adding metal in the proper location. A small amount of metal placed in this way often will increase the rating of the member considerably.

The reinforcement of compression members requiring substantial increases in the sectional area calls for special analysis, the solution depending on the type of section, the details at or near the pins, and other conditions. Metal sometimes may be added to the cover plate, usually between the existing lines of rivets. This should be balanced by placing additional metal on the lower flanges in the manner described in the preceding paragraph. Full-length side plates may be added to the web plates of the section, between the vertical legs of the upper and lower angles, providing adequate means of transferring this stress into the connection or adjacent member can be obtained. If the cover plate in the original design is so wide in proportion to its thickness that it has little resistance to buckling, this may be corrected by adding a cover plate connected by fasteners along the center line in addition to the fasteners through the angles. Often strengthening is solely for the purpose of reducing the slenderness ratio.

One of the problems encountered in reinforcing compression members is to introduce the dead load stress into the additional material. If this is not done, full value cannot be obtained from the new material. For instance, assuming that the new material gets no dead load stress, that the dead load stress in the old material is 10,000 psi, and that the total allowable stress is 26,000 psi, then the new material will be carrying only 16,000 psi stress from live load only. This is the maximum stress to which the new metal can be worked, since any higher stress would cause overstress in the old metal. Several methods may be used to meet this condition. The one most commonly employed in heavy reinforcing members is to calculate the shortening necessary to produce the desired stress under dead load, and then drill the holes in the old and the new members in such posotion that the new members will be shortened by drifting before the sections are bolted or the rivets are driven.

Another method is used on upper chords and end posts. It is wholly different and can be used only for large members. The cover plates may be thin compared with their unsupported width and it is desired to use a method that will bring all of the old metal into full use. The reinforcement, in this case, is provided in the form of a new central web with top and bottom flange angles, but is divided into two segments, each occupying one-half of the panel length. The segments are designed to receive a wedge between their adjacent ends. The segments are placed inside the member with ends bearing against the pins and the wedge. To introduce compression in the segments, the new materal is first seated for proper bearing against the pins or connections by pulling the wedge up tight by means of a large bolt. The wedges are then slacked off and pulled up to a snug fit, after which all the wedges in one chord are drawn up simultaneously a predetermined amount to develop the desired dead load stress in the new metal. The bolts holding the wedges are left in place permanently. The flanges of the new segment are riveted or bolted to the top cover plate and to the lower lacing bars, thus making the new center segment an integral part of the chord, carrying the same stress per square inch as the old metal.

7.1.3.3 Prestressing

One of the most romantic concepts of strengthening a truss bridge is to consider prestressing.

If a single tension member is to be prestressed, then a check of its ability to support the anchoring system and its ability to withstand the compressive force without local or overall buckling will be sufficient. The current condition of the member is important in this evaluation.

If an entire bottom chord, or some other group of members is to be strengthened by prestressing, the effect of the prestressing force on other members must be considered. In many older truss bridges, the web system simply cannot tolerate the resulting forces. The effect of these forces on the floor and bracing systems must also be considered. If the truss details are poor, the chances of success are remote.

7.1.3.4 Adding a Center Truss

The reinforcement of deck truss spans frequently is accomplished by the addition of a center truss. In a single-track bridge, this is comparitively simple, as ample bracing may be applied to make the three trusses deflect alike. The center truss should not be too stiff but should have the same deflection under load as the old trusses. Otherwise excessively heavy cross bracing will be required or else excessive stresses will be induced in the center truss before the outer trusses have deflected enough to stress the members up to their safe carrying capacity.

The addition of a center truss in a double-track deck truss span that has only two trusses, creates difficult problems. The tracks may be loaded either separately or simultaneously, and it is not economical to introduce enough bracing between the trusses to make them act together. The floorbeams will be continuous over the new truss. If the center truss is too stiff, the outer truss will have greater deflection under a single-track load, and the outer rail will be low under load. When both tracks are loaded, however, the center truss shall be strong enough to carry its share of the load from both tracks. Thus the truss deflections and the distribution of stresses through the floorbeams for various conditions of loading should be determined and a design chosen in which the different members will be as nearly as possible under equal stress without introducing objectionable deflections and poor riding track. The reinforcement should be designed in such a way that in erection the new center truss may be swung under its own dead load before making the final connections between the new and the old trusses.

7.1.3.5 Doubling of Truss

Section 1, Figure 2, shows a truss strengthened in this manner. The connection between the floor system and both trusses required special attention. Pony trusses have been strengthened by adding Bailey trusses (69).

7.1.3.6 Auxiliary Truss Supports

Under certain favorable conditions, it is possible to shorten the effective span length of a truss by the installation of auxiliary piers or bents at the first or second interior panel points. However, since this converts a simple span truss to a three-span continuous truss, introducing new and different stress characteristics, a thorough analysis of the altered truss must be made. Members having insufficient capacity must be strengthened to carry the revised loading prior to the installation of the new supports.

As an emergency measure, the erection of supporting falsework may be advisable. However, this should not be a permanent feature because erosion may make the supports ineffective.

7.1.3.7 Auxiliary Truss Members

Girders, lattice trusses, floorbeams and stringers may be reinforced by adding auxiliary truss members underneath to support them at various points.

7.1.3.8 Continuity

It may be possible in some cases to make two or more truss spans into one continuous span. A thorough analysis of the altered trusses is essential. Waddell, p. 1079 (61) described a proposal to convert a set of simple truss spans into a cantilever structure.

7.2 Widening

7.2.1 General

There are three basic methods of widening a truss bridge. The existing trusses may be stretched further apart (Fig. 44), cantilever brackets (Fig. 45) may be added, or an additional longitudinal support system may be added (Fig. 46). These appear in many variations and often combined (Fig. 47). In all cases, the stiffness and load distribution characteristics will change, and strengthening (see Section 7.1) may be required.

7.2.2 Examples

The following examples have proven successful.

7.2.2.1 Deck Widening by Adding Longitudinal Support System

"one of the favored methods of widening an existing truss bridge is to relocate one of the trusses further away from the other and add a pair of plate girders near the previous axis of the relocated truss. The existing floor beams thus span between a truss and one of the plate girders; the other girder and the relocated truss support a new set of floor beams which in turn support the additional width of the bridge. The bridge-widening arrangement mentioned above is shown in Fig. 47.

The resistance of a pony truss against lateral bending of the top chord is little affected by the widening of the deck as per the arrangement shown in Fig. 47 provided that the additional width of the deck is not more than the original deck width."

7.2.2.2 Deck Widening by Increasing Lengths of Transverse Floor Beams

"The width of a pony truss bridge can be increased by cutting the transverse floor beams in the middle, relocating one of the trusses, and inserting additional lengths of floor beams between the two halves of the existing ones as shown in Fig. 44.

If a pony truss bridge is to be widened according to the above mentioned method, a reduction in strength should be expected. Even after the reduction of strength, however, the bridge might still have enough strength to cope with the increased dead load and traffic caused by widening."

7.2.2.3 The existing trusses may be moved closer together and additional trusses placed on each side as shown in Fig. 46. This may eliminate the need for strengthening the existing trusses. In some cases, the existing trusses may be able to support an additional exterior lane without being relocated or strengthened.

7.2.2.4 Cantilever brackets may be added to the outside of the truss (Fig. 45). This may or may not require strengthening.

In all cases, the expedient of adding a new set of spans adjacent to the existing (i.e.: Twinning) should be considered.

7.3 Repair of Bent or Elongated Members

7.3.1 Bent Members

Members of a truss may be bent by vehicle impact, by impact of debris during floods, or by buckling due to overload. For members under tension or low compression loads, bent member may be straightened in place by combined thermal expansion and contraction (69, 70, 71). By heating the member in a particular fashion, namely a "V" shape area, the metal not in direct contact with the heat will supply resistance to thermal expansion (Figure 48). This restrained thermal expansion is the basic principle of the heat-straightening method. An oxyacetylene torch applies heat up to 1200 °F. Steel heated to this degree would normally expand; however, by applying the heat first to the bottom point of the "V" and slowly progressing outwards, upsetting occurs in the immediate area of heating because of the above mentioned resistance to thermal expansion. The purpose of using a "V" area is that upsetting is increased proportionately as the heat is applied and moved to the outer edge of the "V". Therefore, more upsetting may be caused in the elongated portion of a bent member. After cooling the member will tend to straighten out. Subsequent "heats" may be needed to complete the straightening procedure.

Bent members subjected to significant compression should not be straightened using only heat because of potential buckling. A jacking force perpendicular to the member together with the V-heating is effective in straightening compression members.

Hammer peening of the elongated side of the bent member will enhance the straightening process. The peening lowers the yield stress of the strain-hardened material and it helps eliminate high residual stresses.

7.3.2 Elongated Members

California, Louisiana and Virginia (69) have successfully restored initial tension forces to eye bars which have been elongated due to being bent or overloaded. The bent area is straightened first, then as shown in Figure 49, a yoke is fastened around the bar. The area within the yoke is uniformly heated to between 1600 °F and 1800 °F, "cherry red". The bar is upset by tightening the nuts of the yoke. California DOT gauges the desired tension by dynamically measuring the bars natural frequency (higher frequencies mean higher tension). Subsequent "heats" may be needed to attain the desired tension.

8. SUMMARY AND CONCLUSIONS

A summary of existing procedures have been presented in the determination of the load capacity of steel truss bridges. These procedures involve both analytical and experimental methods.

Techniques have also been presented to upgrade or strengthen the bridges which are rated low. Further methods are warranted however, if these bridges are to be functional in the future.

9. RESEARCH NEEDS

The problems associated with many old truss bridges, particularly those on secondary highways and local roads, stem primarily from age. The structures were designed for relatively light loadings; have narrow roadways that are inadequate for present traffic; and are often the victims of ineffective maintenance. Faced with these problems many authorities see no choice beyond replacement of old trusses as rapidly as funds become available. Research to develop alternatives to replacement would be most beneficial because of the scarcity of funds. Several broad areas of research can be suggested.

1. Practical techniques must be developed for increasing the structural capacity of old truss bridges. Ideally, consideration should be given not only to restoring the original strength of the structure, as has sometimes been done, but to increasing the capacity to a level above the design loading.
2. Cost-effective methods for improving the geometrics, including consideration of both horizontal and vertical clearances, are needed if many old truss bridges are to carry today's traffic.
3. Lightweight deck systems, rails, and other appurtenances must be developed and evaluated to allow reduction of dead load and to upgrade the safety of existing truss bridges.
4. Exact methods of analysis with particular attention to the stress distribution in connections and other details would be beneficial in providing a true assessment of the strength of an existing truss.
5. Economical repair procedures for the long-term relief of common types of distress must be developed to replace the "band-aid" techniques so often employed.

6. Research has begun to realize the value of many existing trusses as historical artifacts. Surveys of existing trusses, using guidelines available from federal agencies, should be made to ascertain the significance of older trusses. Given the pressure toward bridge replacement, this need may be critical.

Many of these items are included within the scope of ongoing research efforts, and, as indicated in this report, there are several instances in which some of the needs have been successfully met. However, the problem is so widespread and the varieties of trusses so diverse that additional research is warranted. Detailed reporting of successful measures that have been employed by various agencies to increase the structural or traffic carrying capacity of older truss bridges may be as beneficial as developmental work at this time.

10. REFERENCES

1. Barton, J. R., Kusenberger, F. N. and Birchak, J. R., "Development of a New System for Detecting Fatigue Cracks in Steel Bridges," Federal Highway Administration, Report No. FHWA-RD-73-89, 1973.

2. Bigelow, Lawrence N., "Fifty-Year Development-Construction of Steel Truss Bridges," Journal of the Construction Division, ASCE, Vol. 101, No. CO2, Proc. Paper 11381, June 1975, pp. 239-258.

3. "Bridge Inspector's Training Manual. "U.S. Dept. of Transportation Federal Highway Administration, Bureau of Public Roads, Washington D.C., 1970.

4. Byers, William G., "Rating and Reliability of Railway Bridges," Methods of Structural Analysis, edited by Wm. E. Saul & Alain H. Peyrot, ASCE, New York, 1976, pp. 153-169.

5. Elleby, Hottern A., Sanders, Wallace W., Klaiber, F. Wayne and Reeves, M. Douglas, "Service Load and Fatigue Tests on Truss Bridges," Journal of the Structural Division, ASCE, Vol. 102, No. ST12, Proc. Paper 12625, December 1976, pp. 2285-2300.

6. Fisher, John W., "Bridge Fatigue Guide-Design and Details," American Institute of Steel Construction, N.Y., 1977.

7. "Highway Accident Report-Collapse of U.S. 35 Highway Bridge, Point Pleasant, West Virginia, December 15, 1967," Report No. NTSB-HAR-71-1, National Transportation Safety Board, U.S. Dept. of Commerce, NTIS, Springfield, Va., 1970.

8. "Inspection of Steel Bridges for Fatigue Damage," Subcommittee on Inspection of Steel Bridges for Fatigue of the Task Committee on Structural Fatigue of the Structural Division of ASCE, Paper 8321, Proceedings of ASCE, Vol. 97 ST8, August 1971, pp. 2107-2118.

9. "Manual for Maintenance Inspection of Bridges," American Association of State Highway Officials, Washington, 1974.

10. "Progress in Design of Steel Bridge Details," American Railway Engineering Association Committee 15-Iron and Steel Structures, Proceedings, American Railway Engineering Association, Vol. 41, 1940, pp. 412-444.

11. Sanders, Wallace W., Klaiber, F., Wayne, Elleby, Hottern A. and Timm, Leonard W., "Ultimate Load Test of Truss Bridge Floor System," Journal of the Structural Division, ASCE, Vol. 102, No. ST7, Proc. Paper 12247, July 1976, pp. 1383-1398.

12. Scott, M. B., Cox J. W., "Further Study of the Behavior of Floorbeam Hangers-Static Stress Measurements on the AT&SF Railway Bridge near Ponca City, Oklahoma," AREA Proceedings, V. 53, 1952, pp. 35-63.

13. "Secondary Stresses," American Railway Engineering Association Committee 15-Iron and Steel Structures, Proceedings, American Railway Engineering Association, Vol. 15, 1914, pp. 427-491.

14. "The Shortening of Eyebars to Equalize the Stress," American Railway Engineering Association, Committee 15-Iron and Steel Structures, Proceedings, American Railway Engineering Association, Vol. 48, 1947, pp. 969-986.

15. "Steel Structures-Sec. 7.4 Inspection," Manual for Railway Engineering American Railway Engineering Association, Chicago, 1973, pp. 15-7-15 to 15-7-21.

16. Wiley, L. T. et al, "A Study of the Behavior of Floorbeam Hangers-Static and Dynamic Stress Measurements on the Illinois Central Railroad Bridge at Galena, Ill.," AREA Proceedings, Vol. 51, 1950, pp. 51-73.

17. Baidar Bakht, "1978 Bridge Testing," Ministry of Transportation and Communications of Ontario, Downsview, Research Report, to be published.

18. Arthur Bolton, "A Quick Approximation to the Critical Load of Rigidly Jointed Trusses," The Structural Engineer, March 1955.

19. Csagoly, P. and Bahkt, B., 1978. "A Computer Program to Determine the Collapse Load of Steel Trusses," Ministry of Transportation and Communications of Ontario, Downsview. Research Report to be published.

20. N. J. Hoff, Bruno A. Boley, S. V. Nardo and Sara Kaufman, "Buckling at Rigid Jointed Plane Trusses," American Society of Civil Engineers, Vol. 76, June 1950.

21. S. P. Timoshenko and J. M. Gere, "Theory of Elastic Stability," McGraw Hill Book Company, 1961.

22. Martin, H. C. and Carey, C. F., "Introduction to Finite Element Analysis," McGraw Hill Book Company, 1973.

23. Hambley, E. C., "Bridge Deck Behavior," Chapman and Hall, London, England, 1976.

24. Batchelor, B. deV. and Hewitt, B. E., "Direct Model Studies of Some Reinforced Concrete Structures," accepted for presentation at First Australian Conference on Structural Models, University of Sydney, (1972).

25. Batchelor, B. deV., and Tong, P. Y., "An Investigation of the Ultimate Shear Strength of Two-Way Continuous Bridge Slabs Subjected to Concentrated Loads," Department of Highways-Ontario, Report No. RR167, (1970).

26. Hewitt, B. E., "An Investigation of the Punching Strength of Restrained Slabs with Particular Reference to the Deck Slabs of Composite I-Beam Bridges," Ph.D. Tehsis, Queen's University, Kingston (1972).

27. Hewitt, B. E. and Batchelor, B. deV., "Punching Shear Strength of Restrained Slabs, Journal of the Structural Division, Proceedings of the American Society of Civil Engineers, Vol. 101, No. ST9, (1975).

28. Csagoly, P. F., Holowka, M. and Dorton, R., "The True Behavior of Concrete Thin Slabs," paper submitted for TRB Bridge Conference in Missouri, 1978.

29. Batchelor, B. deV., Hewitt, B. E., Csagoly, P. F. and Holowka, M., "An Investigation of the Ultimate Strength of Deck Slabs of Composite Steel/Concrete Bridges," paper submitted for TRB Bridge Conference in Missouri, 1978.

30. Bakht, B., Cheung, M. S. and Aziz, T. S., "Application of a Simplified Method of Calculating Longitudinal Moments to the Proposed Ontario Highway Bridge Design Code," submitted for publication to the Canadian Journal of Civil Engineering.

31. Bakht, B. and Csagoly, P., "Testing of Perley Bridge," Research Report No. 207, Ministry of Transportation and Communications of Ontario, Downsview, January 1977.

32. Billing, J. R. and Agarwal, A. C., "Dynamic Test and Analysis of Tansley and Conestogo River Bridges," Research Report, Ministry of Transportation and Communications of Ontario, Downsview. To be published in 1978.

33. Csagoly, P. and Bakht, B., "In-plane Buckling of Steel Truss Bridges," to be submitted to the Journal of Canadian Society for Civil Engineering.

34. Csagoly, P. and Bakht, B., "Lateral Buckling of Pony Truss Bridges," Transportation Research Board 607, Washington, D.C. 1976.

35. Dorton, R. A. and Csagoly, P., "The Development of the Ontario Bridge Code," Paper prepared for the 1977 National Lecture Tour of the Canadian Society for Civil Engineering, Structural Division, Ministry of Trans. and Communications of Ontario, Downsview, October 1977.

36. West, R., 1973, "The Use of Grillage Analogy for the Analysis of Slab and Pseudoslab Bridge Decks," Research Report No. 21, Cement and Concrete Association, London, England.

37. Sanders, W. W., Jr. Elleby, H. A. and Klaiber, F. W., "Ultimate Load Behavior of Full-Scale Highway Truss Bridges," Summary Report, Engineering Research Institute, Iowa State University, Ames, Sept. 1975.

38. Sanders, W. W., Jr. Klaiber, F. W., Ellby, H. A. and Timm, L. W., "Ultimate Load Test of Truss Bridge Floor Systems," Journal of the Structural Division, ASCE, July 1976.

39. Sweeney, R.A.P., "The Load Spectrum for the Fraser River Bridge at New Westminister, B.C.," Area Bulletin 658, p. 561-577, June-July 1976.

40. Fisher, J. W. and Daniels, J. H., An Investigation of the Estimated Fatigue Damage in Members of the 380 ft. Main Span, Fraser River Bridge," AREA Bulletin 658, p. 577-597, June-July 1976.

41. Sweeney, R.A.P., "The Importance of Redundancy in Bridge Fracture Control," T.R.B. Meeting, January 1979.

42. Galambos, C. F. and Armstrong, W. L., "Loading History of Highway Bridges," Highway Research Record 295, 1969, p. 85-98.

43. "A Guide for the Field Testing of Bridges, ASCE Technical Committee on Structural Safety and Reliability," in preparation.

44. Heins, C. P., "Field Measurements and Load Spectra of Highway Bridges," from Methods of Structural Analysis, p. 133-152, ASCE 1976.

45. Gurney, T. R., "Fatigue of Welded Structures," Cambridge University Press, 1968.

46. Sweeney, R.A.P., "Some Examples of Detection and Repair of Fatigue Damage in Railway Bridge Members," T.R.B. Annual Meeting, January 1978.

47. "Replacement or Repair of Old Truss Bridges," C.P. Heins, W.S. Fout, R. Y. Wilkison, TR Record 607, TRB, National Academy of Sciences, January 1976.

48. Sanders, W. W., Elleby, H. A. and Klaiber, F. W., "Ultimate Load Behavior of Full-Scale Highway Truss Bridges: Phase II - Service Load and Supplementary Tests," Final Report, Engineering Research Institute, Iowa State University, Ames, August 1975.

49. Sanders, W. W., Klaiber, F. W., Elleby, H. A. and Timm, L. W., "Ultimate Load Behavior of Full-Scale Highway Truss Bridges: Phase I - Ultimate Load Tests of the Hubby - Boone County," Final Report, Engineering Research Institute, Iowa State University, Ames, April 1975.

50. Klaiber, F. W., Sanders, W. W., and Elleby, H. A., "Ultimate Load Test of High Truss Bridge," Transportation Research Record No. 607, 1976, pp. 75-80.

51. "LongsMill Road Over Owens Creek - Bridge No. 4-4, Bridge Inspection and Rating Report for Frederick County Highway Department," N.K. Dean Assoc., Bel Air, Maryland, 1973.

52. "Daysville Road Over Israel Creek - Bridge No. 26-2, Bridge Inspection and Rating Report for Frederick County Highway Department," N.K. Dean Assoc., Bel Air, Maryland, 1973.

53. "Water Street Over Israel Creek - Bridge No. 26-1, Bridge Inspection and Rating Report for Frederick County Highway Department," N.K. Dean Assoc., Bel Air, Maryland 1973.

54. "Crum Road Over Israel Creek - Bridge No. 26-5, Bridge Inspection and Rating Report for Frederick County Highway Department," N.K. Dean Assoc., Bel Air, Maryland 1973.

55. "Gapland Road Over Broad Run - Bridge No. 22-2, Bridge Inspection and Rating Report for Frederick County Highway Department," N.K. Dean Assoc., Bel Air, Maryland 1973.

56. "Old Hagerstown Road Over Little Catoctin Creek - Bridge No. 3-1 , Bridge Inspection and Rating Report for Frederick County Highway Dept.," N.K. Dean Assoc., Bel Air, Maryland 1973.

57. "AREA Manual," Chapter 15, Section 7.2, AREA, Chicago, Ill.

58. "Instructions for Classification of Steel Bridges and Rolling Stock," CN Rail, KOS-16.1A, Revised 1970 by R.A.P. Sweeney.

59. 1977 Interim Specifications, Bridges, AASHTO, Washington, D.C.

60. Manual for Railway Engineering, Chapter 15, Steel Structures, AREA Chicago, Ill.

61. Waddell, J.A.L., "Bridge Engineering," Volumes 1 and 2, 1916, J. Wiley and Sons, New York, N.Y.

62. Waddell, J.A.L., "De Pontibut," 2nd Edition, 1914, J. Wiley and Sons, New York, N.Y.

63. Roberts, R., Irwin, G. R. and others, "Fracture Toughness of Bridge Steels, Phase II Report," Final Report Sept. 1974, No. FHWA-RD-74-59, N.T.I.S., Springfield, Virginia .

64. Annual Book of ASTM Standards, ASTM, Philadelphia, Pa. (Society founded in 1898).

65. Fisher, J. W., "Bridge Fatigue Guide," AISC 1977, New York, N.Y.

66. Fisher, J. W., "Fatigue Cracking in Bridges From Out-of-Plane Displacements, Canadian Structural Engineering Conference, 1978.

67. "Replacement of Corroded Bridge Truss Members," The Railway Gazette, May 17, 1963.

68. Bakht, Baider and Csagoly, P.F., "Strengthening and Widening of Steel Pony Truss Bridges," Canadian Journal of Civil Engineering, Vol. 4, No. 2, June 1977.

69. Freeman, M.G. and Kahn, L. F., "Repair of Strengthening of Old Metal Truss Bridges," School of Civil Engineering, Georgia Institute of Technology, Atlanta, Georgia, October 1978.

70. Harrison, H. L., "Straightening Structural Members in Place," The Welding Journal, May 1952, pp. 257-267.

71. Holt, R. E., "Flame Straightening Basics," Welding Engineer, September 1965.

LIST OF FIGURES

Fig. 1 TRAVERSE BEAM FLOOR SYSTEM

Fig. 2 SPAN WITH DOUBLED TRUSSES

Fig. 3. FLOOR BEAM ATTACHMENT TO DOUBLED TRUSSES

Fig. 4. SEGMENTAL ROLLER EXPANSION SHOE

Fig. 5(a) TOP: RIVET HEAD STRUCK FIRMLY TO DEVELOP ANY PLAY IN HOLES

Fig. 5(b) BOTTOM: RIVET HEAD TAPPED LIGHTLY IN OPPOSITE DIRECTION TO DETECT MOVEMENT.

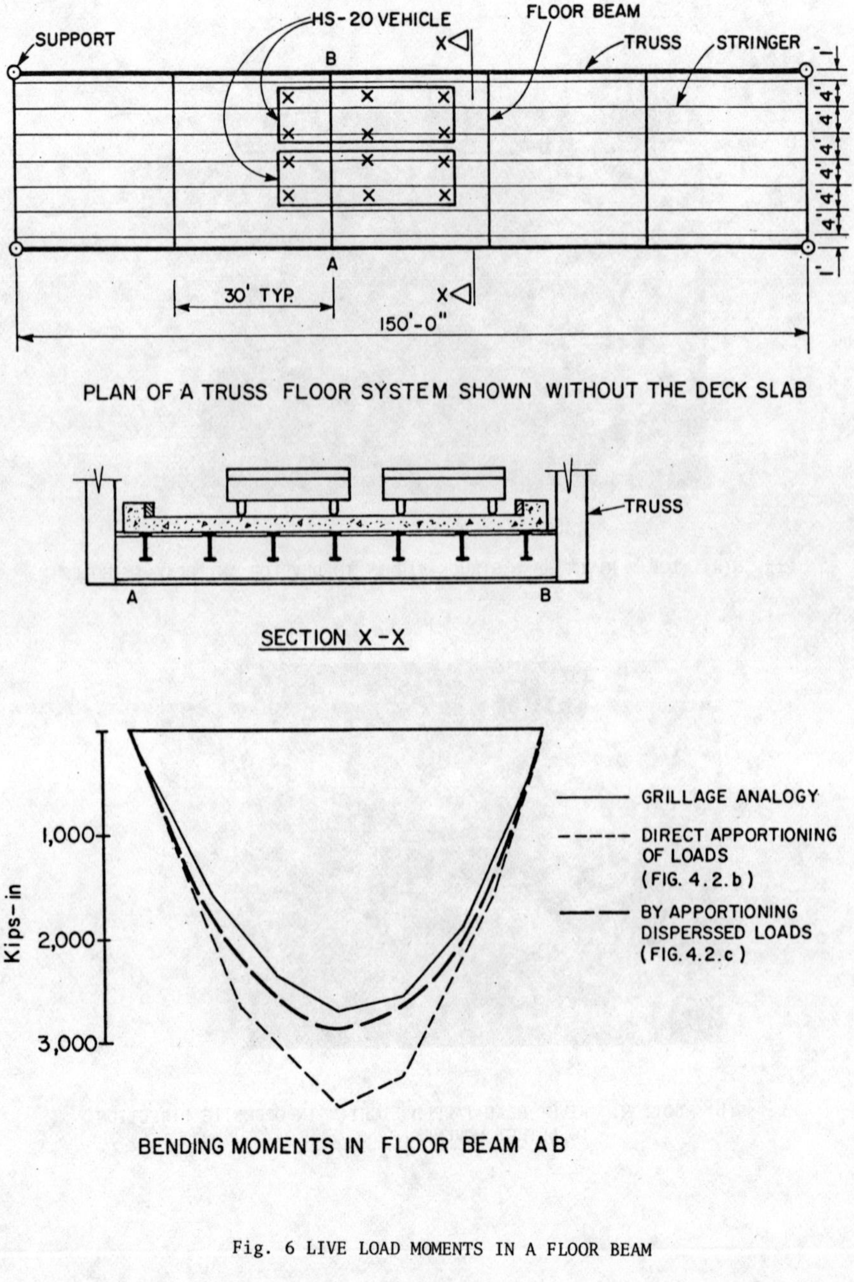

Fig. 6 LIVE LOAD MOMENTS IN A FLOOR BEAM

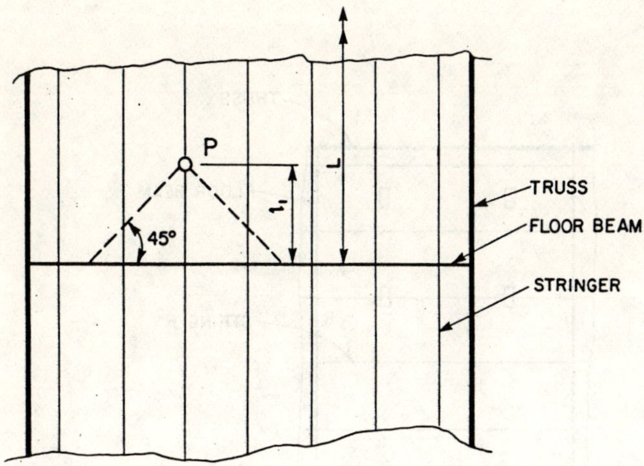

a) PARTIAL PLAN OF FLOOR SYSTEM

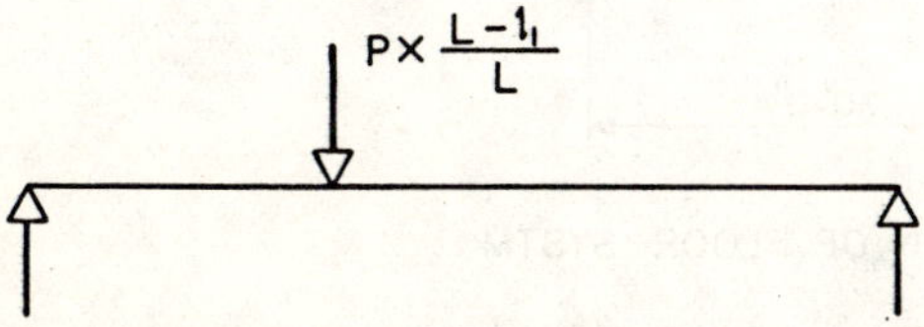

b) LOAD ON FLOOR BEAM BY USUAL PRACTICE

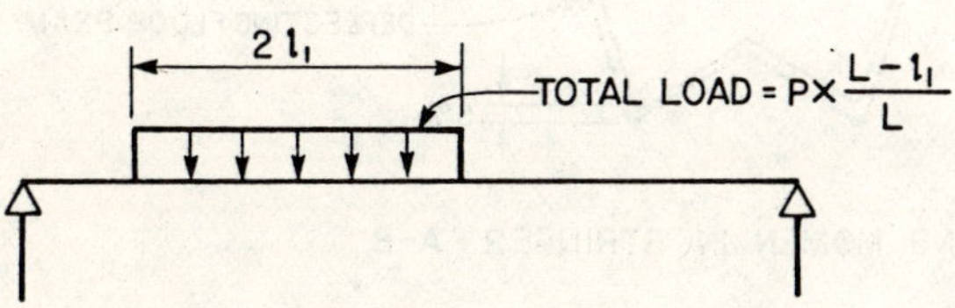

c) LOAD ON FLOOR BEAM BY SUGGESTED SIMPLIFIED APPROACH

Fig. 7 LOAD DISTRIBUTION TO FLOOR BEAMS

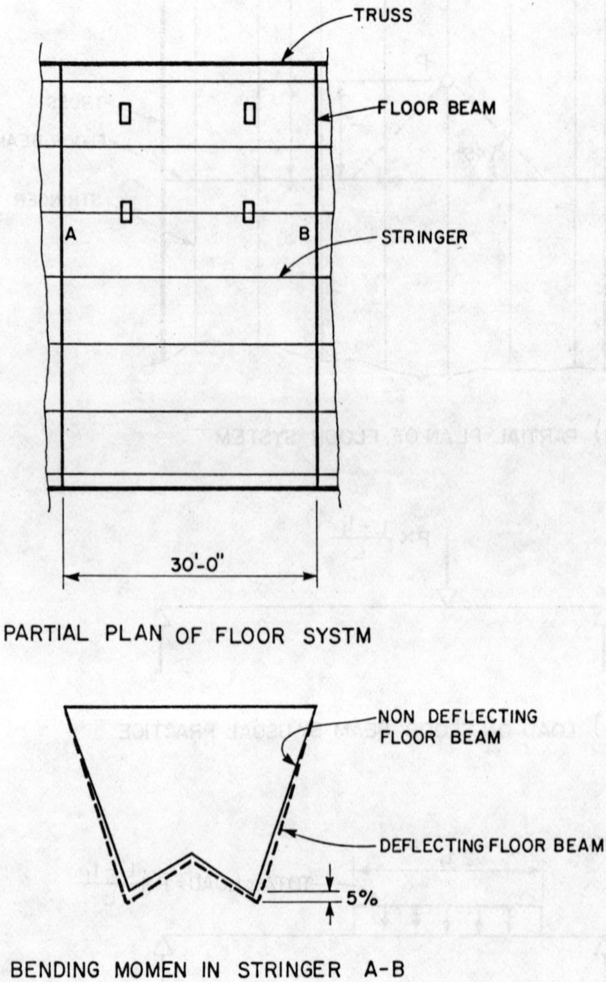

Fig. 8 LIVE LOAD MOMENTS IN A STRINGER

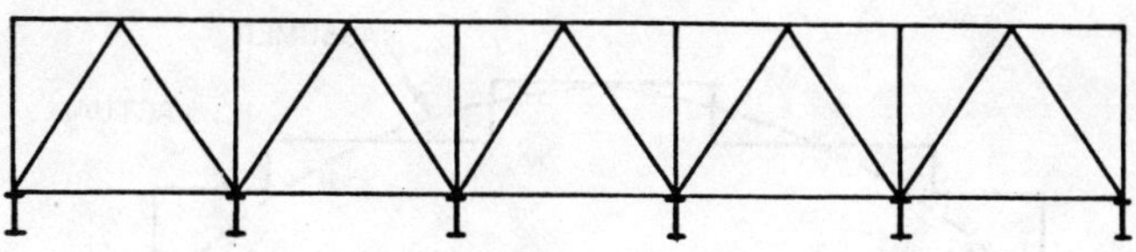

a. A TYPICAL EUROPEAN PONY TRUSS

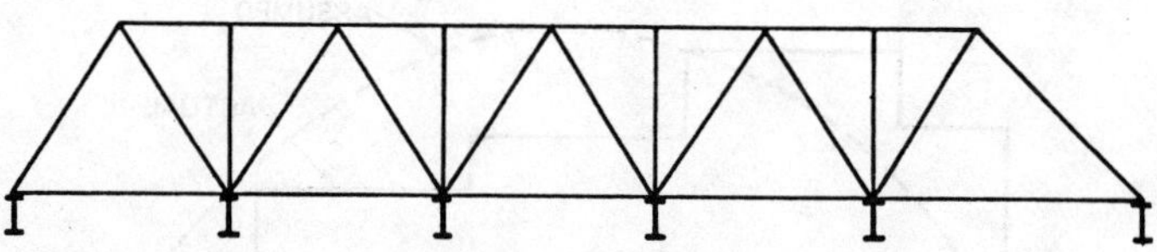

b. A TYPICAL NORTH AMERICAN PONY TRUSS

Fig. 9 PONY TRUSSES

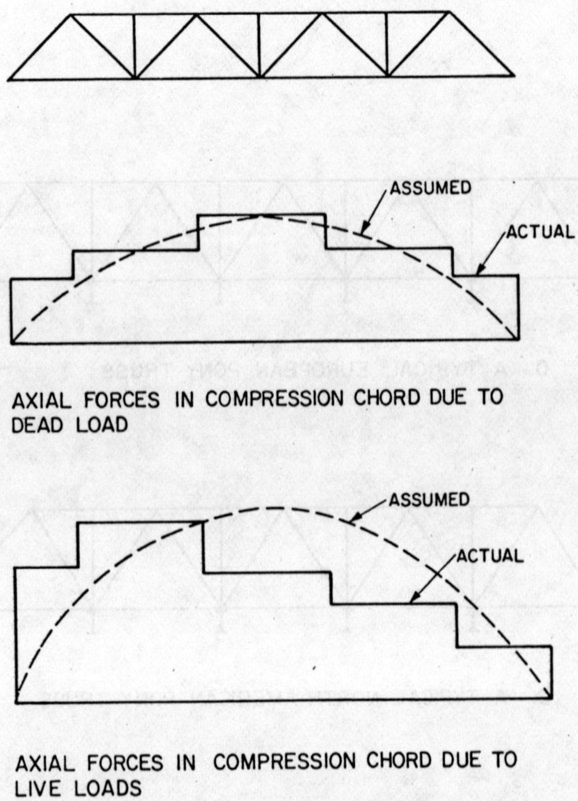

Fig. 10 AXIAL COMPRESSIVE FORCES IN A COMPRESSIVE CHORD

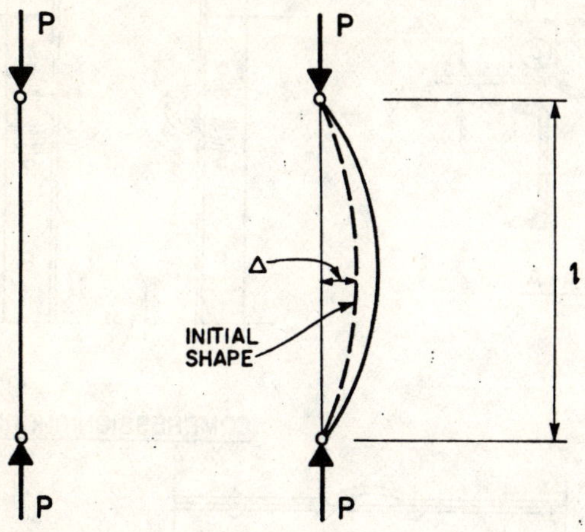

Fig. 11 STRAIGHT AND DEFORMED COLUMNS

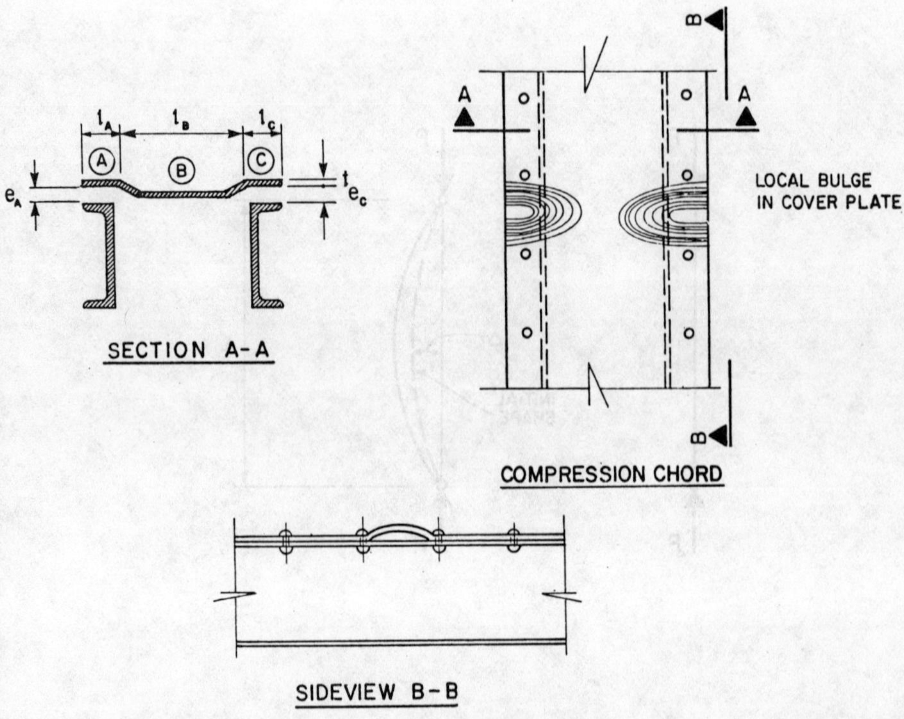

Fig. 12 PORTION OF A BUILT-UP COMPRESSION CHORD

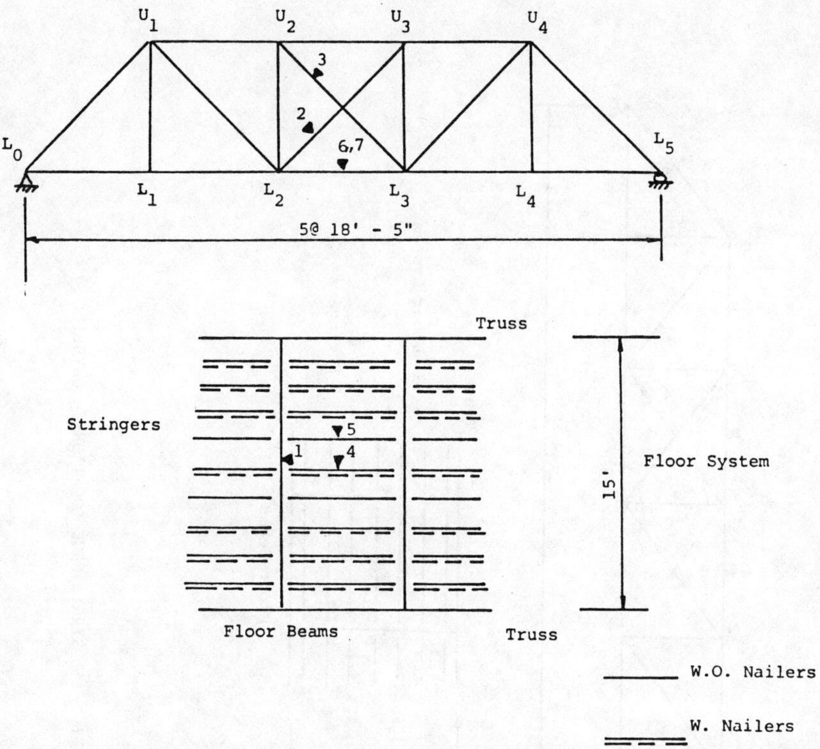

Fig. 13 STRAIN GAGE LOCATIONS - LONGS MILL

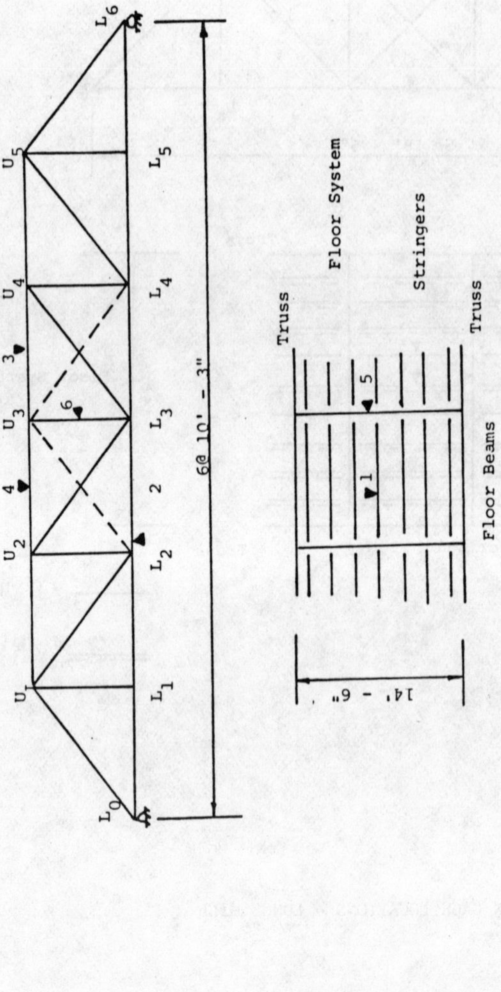

Fig. 14 STRAIN GAGE LOCATIONS - DAYSVILLE

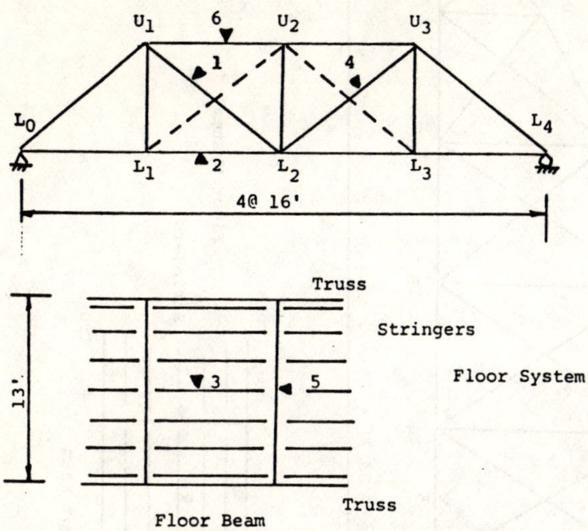

Fig. 15 STRAIN GAGE LOCATIONS - WATER STREET

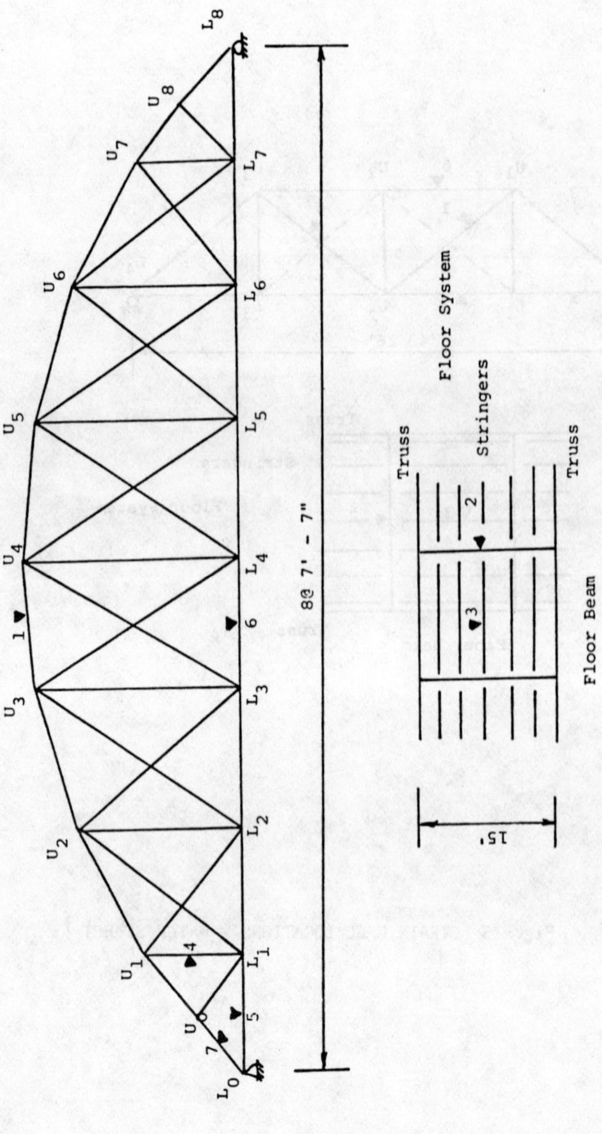

Fig. 16 STRAIN GAGE LOCATIONS - CRUM ROAD

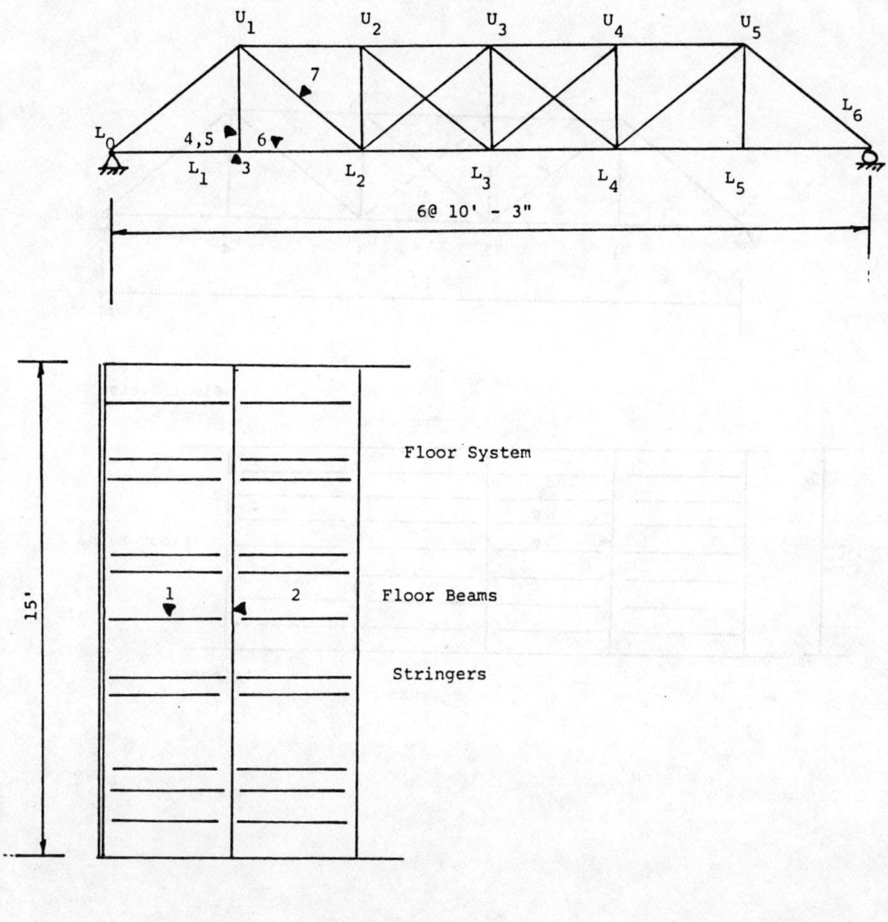

Fig. 17 STRAIN GAGE LOCATIONS - GAPLAND

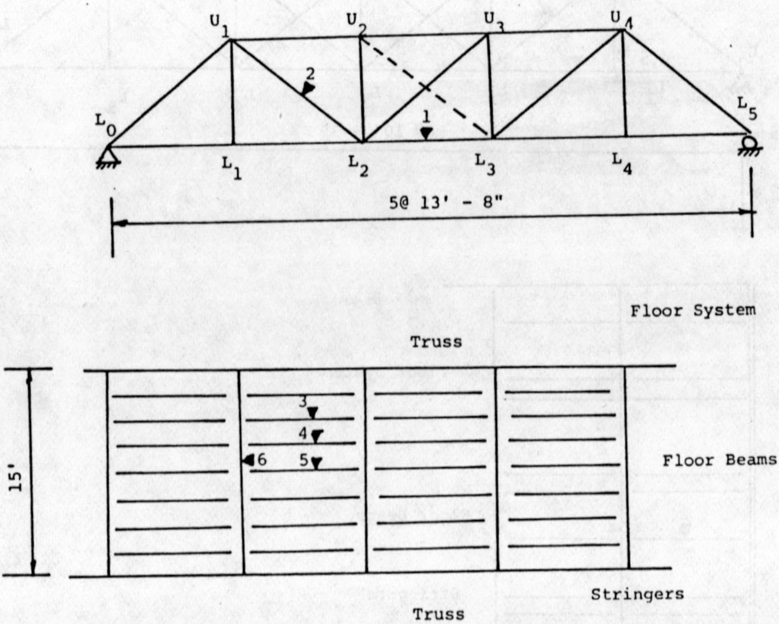

Fig. 18 STRAIN GAGE LOCATIONS - OLD HAGERSTOWN

Fig. 19 STRAIN GAGE LOCATIONS - BOTTOM CHORD

Fig. 20 TRUCK LOADING

Fig. 21 HUBBY BRIDGE

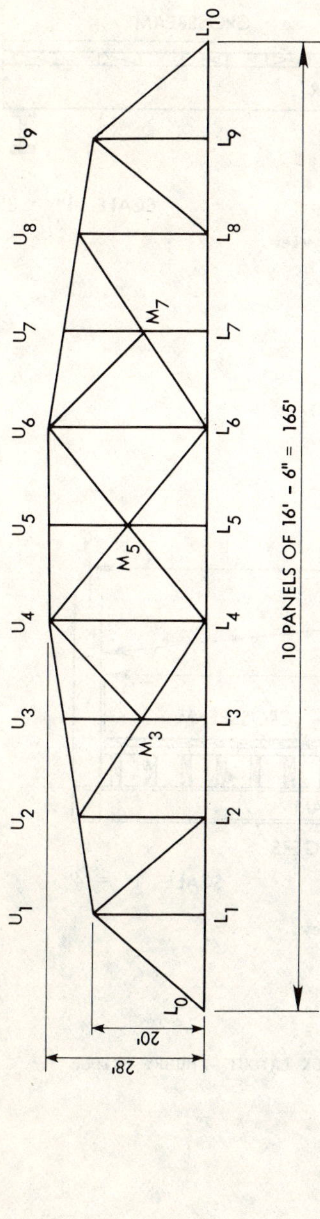

Member layout.

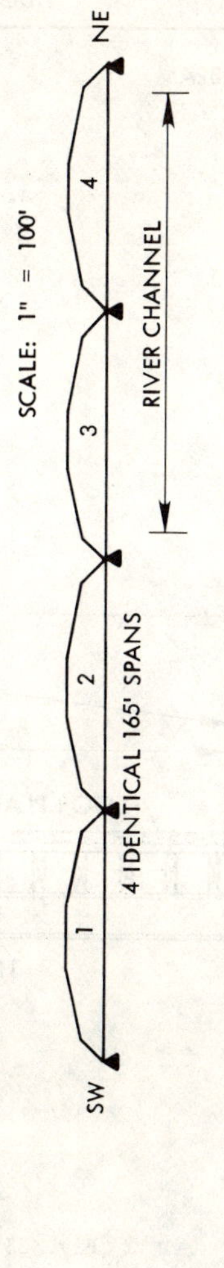

General layout.

Fig. 22 DETAILS OF THE HUBBY BRIDGE

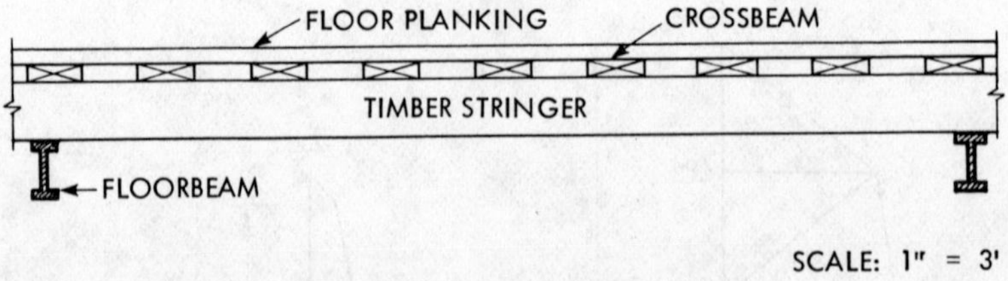

a. Elevation view.

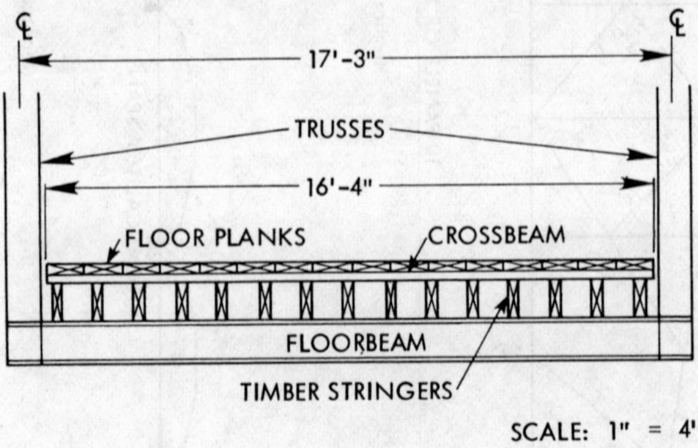

b. End view.

Fig. 23 TIMBER DECK LAYOUT - HUBBY BRIDGE

Fig. 24 CHESTNUT FORD BRIDGE

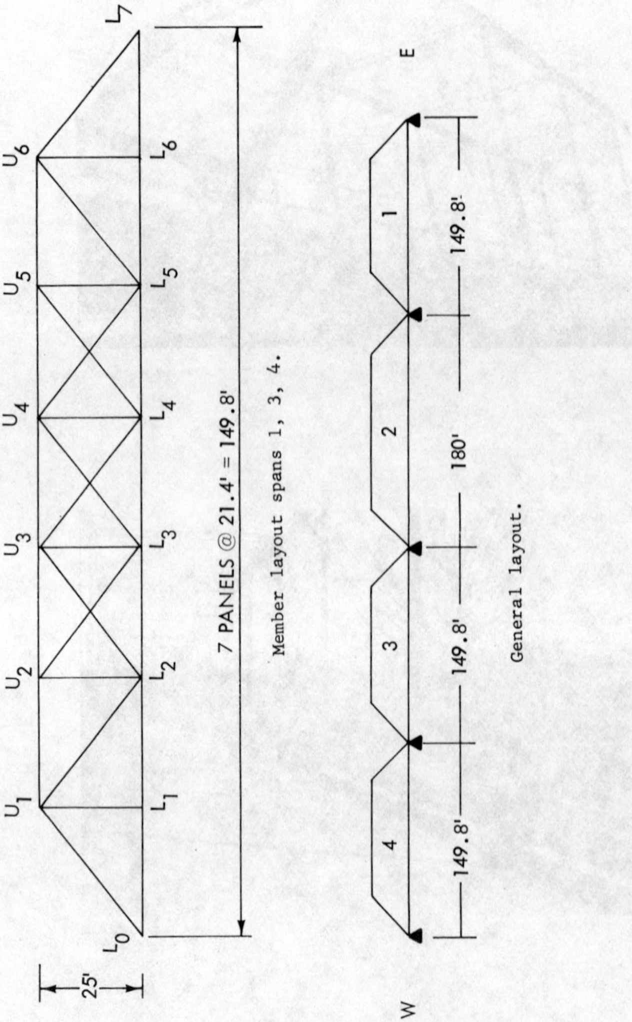

Fig. 25 DETAILS OF THE CHESTNUT FORD BRIDGE

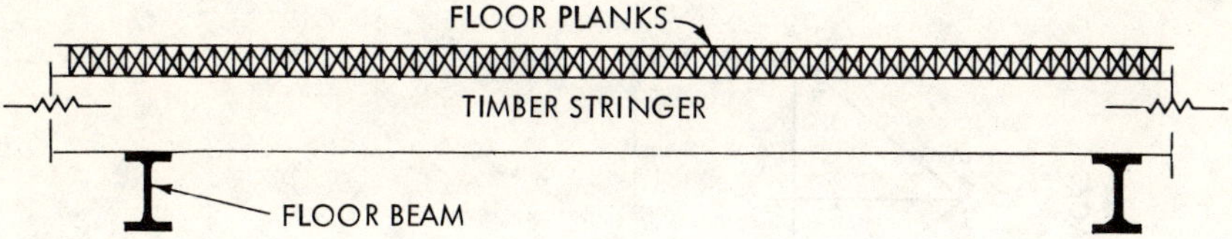

a. Elevation view.

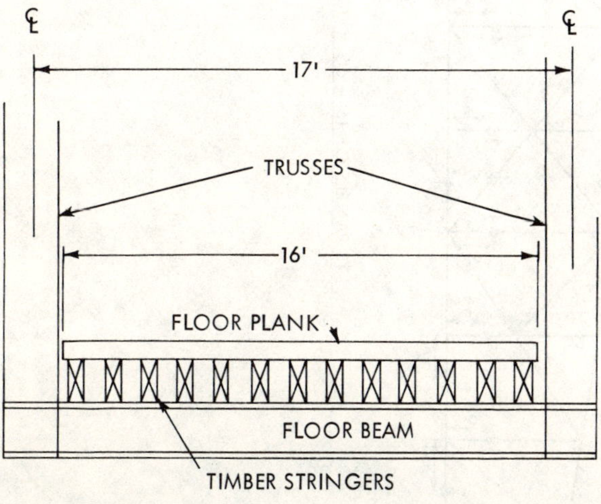

b. End view.

Fig. 26 TIMBER DECK LAYOUT - CHESTNUT FORD BRIDGE

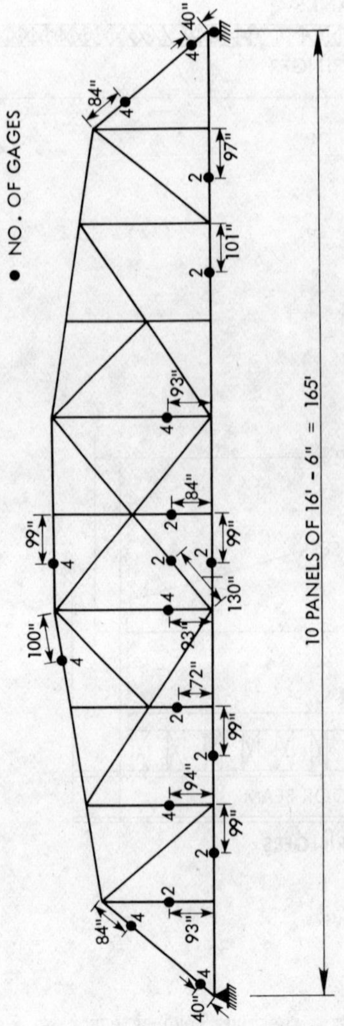

Fig. 27 LOCATION OF STRAIN GAGES ON SPAN Z

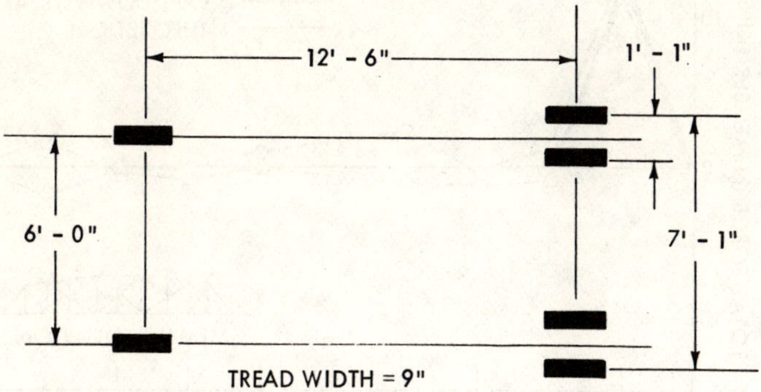

Fig. 19. Description of truck for Hubby Bridge testing.

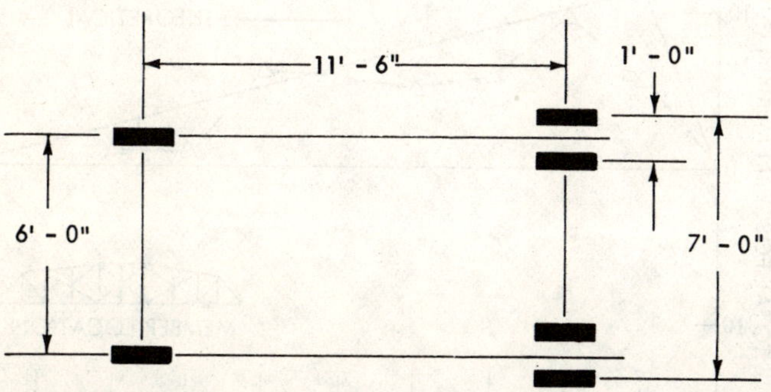

Fig. 28 TEST TRUCK FOR CHESTNUT FORD BRIDGE

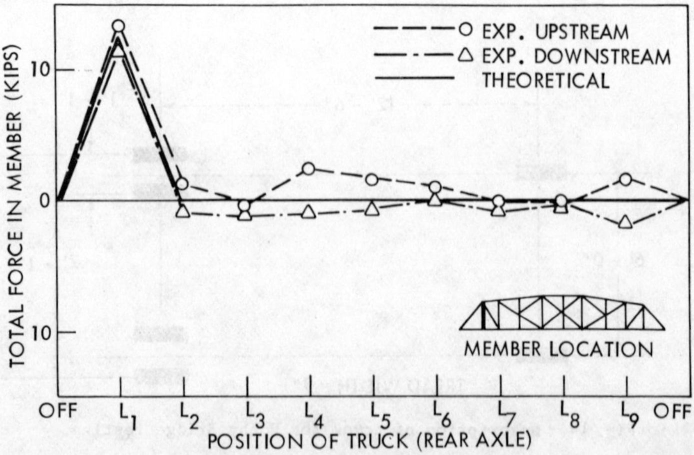

a. Member L_1U_1.

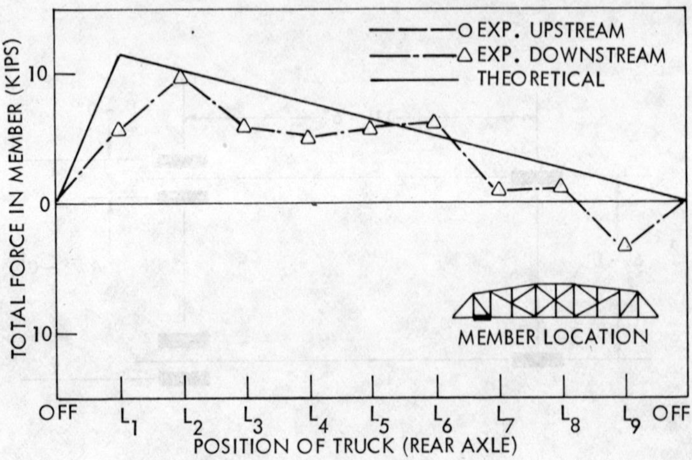

b. Member L_1L_2.

Fig. 29 INFLUENCE LINES FOR SPAN 1 - HUBBY BRIDGE

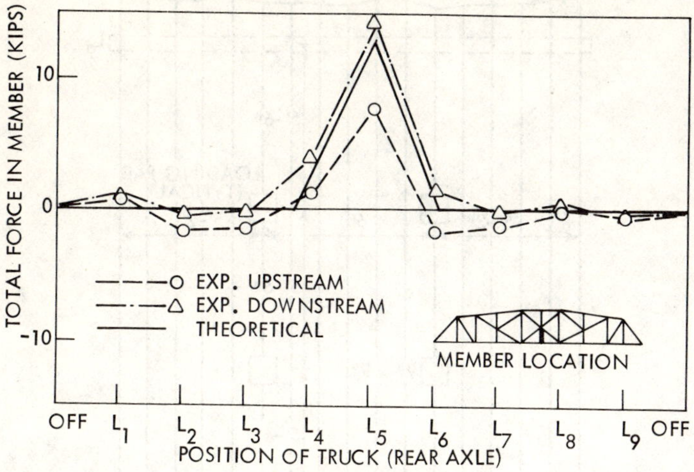

c. Member L_5M_5.

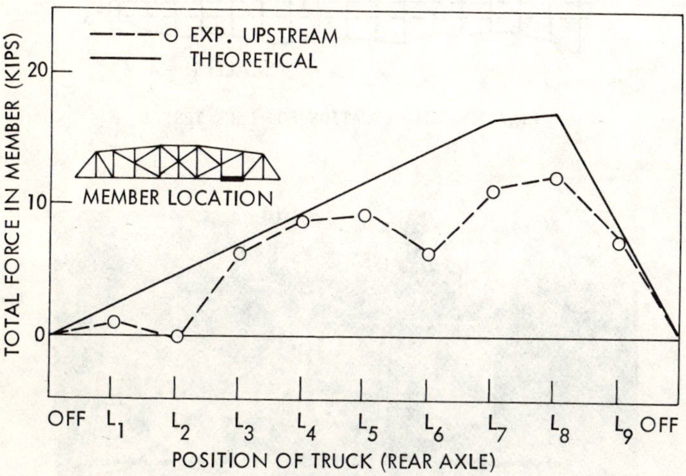

d. Member L_7L_8.

Fig. 29 INFLUENCE LINES FOR SPAN 1 - HOBBY BRIDGE

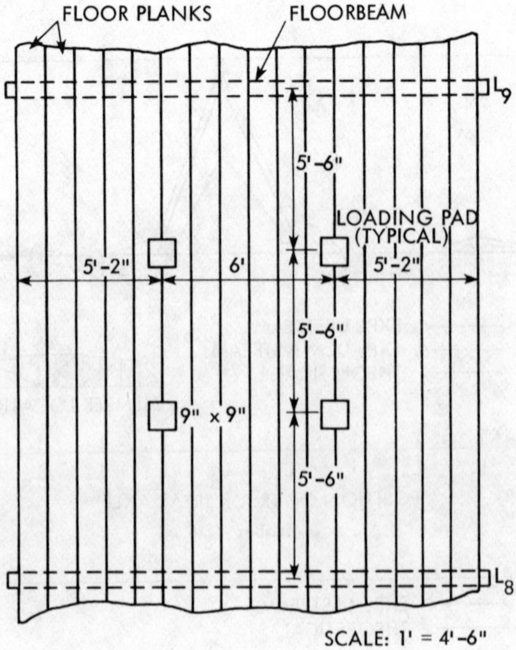

Fig. 30 LOAD LOCATION FOR DECK TEST 1

Fig. 31 DECK TEST 1 SETUP

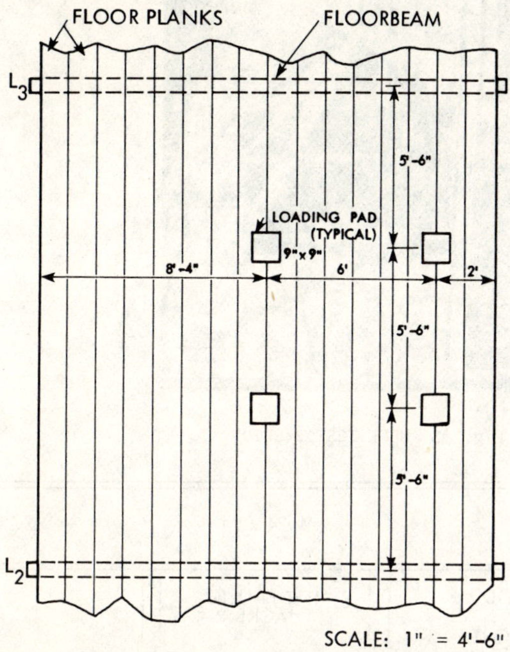

Fig. 32 LOAD LOCATION FOR DECK TEST 2

Fig. 33 DECK TEST 2 SETUP

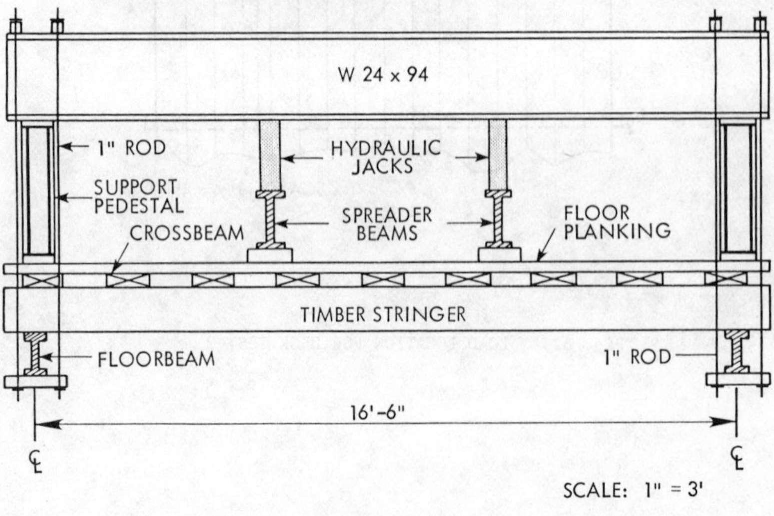

Fig. 34 DECK TEST SETUP

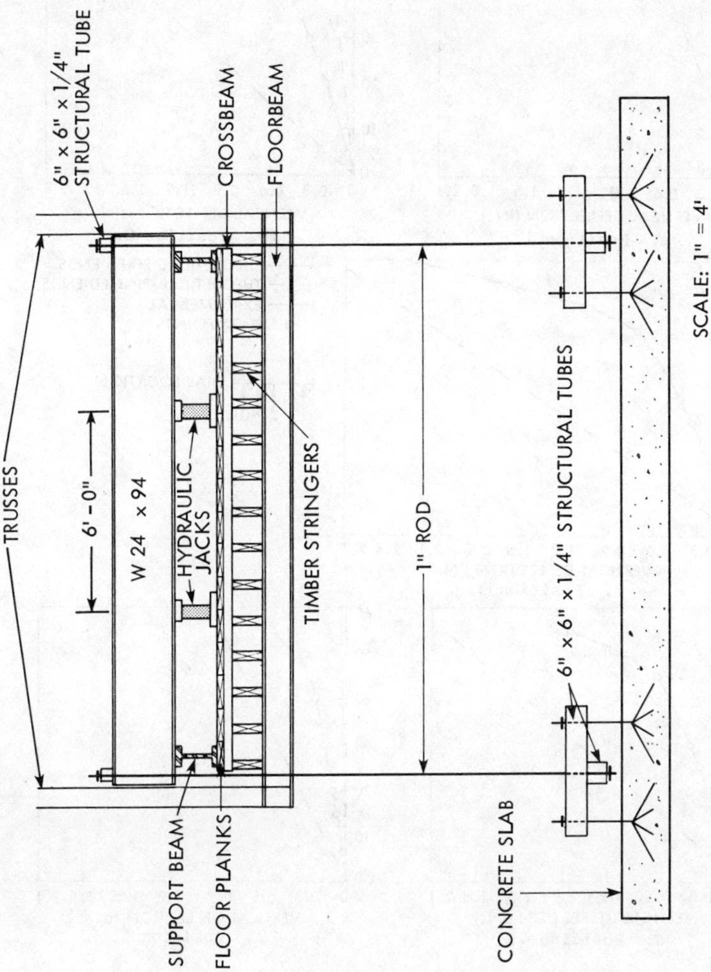

Fig. 35 FLOOR BEAM TEST SETUP

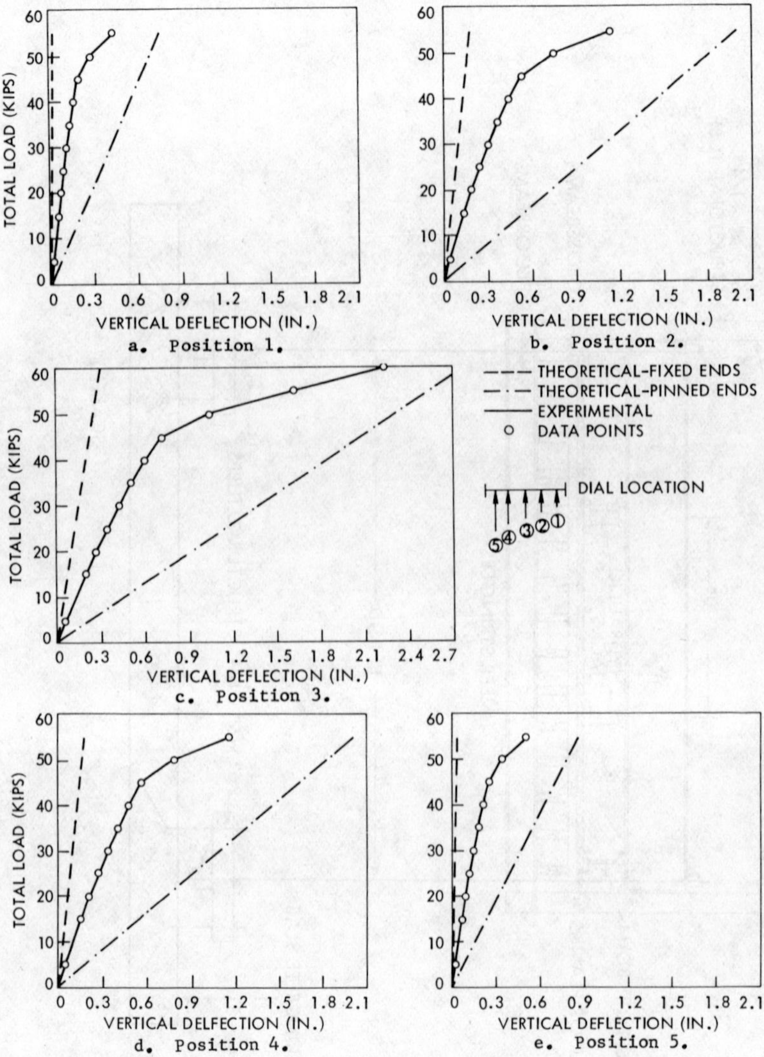

Fig. 36 LOAD-DEFLECTION FOR FLOORBEAM TEST AT L_4.

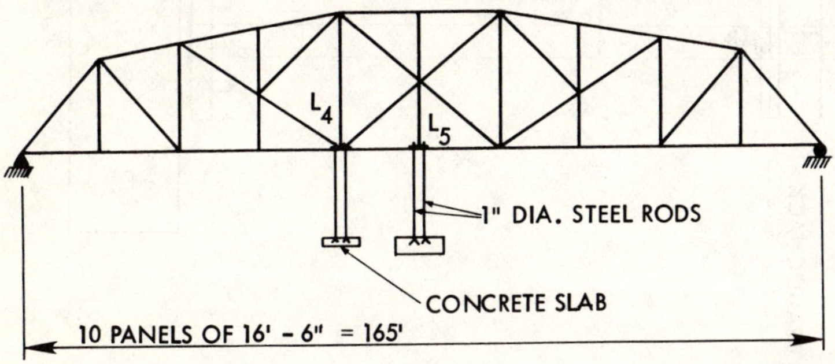

Fig. 37 GENERAL TRUSS VIEW SHOWING LOADING SYSTEM

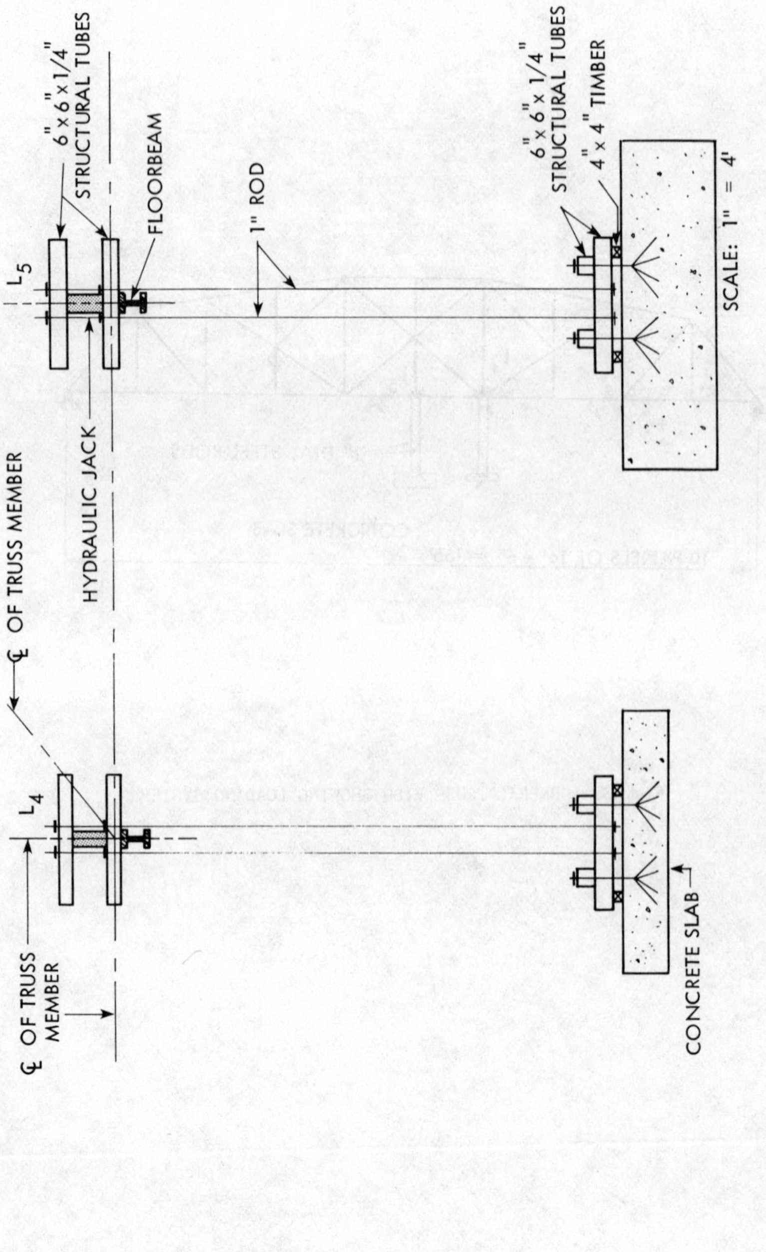

Fig. 38 LOADING SYSTEM DETAILS

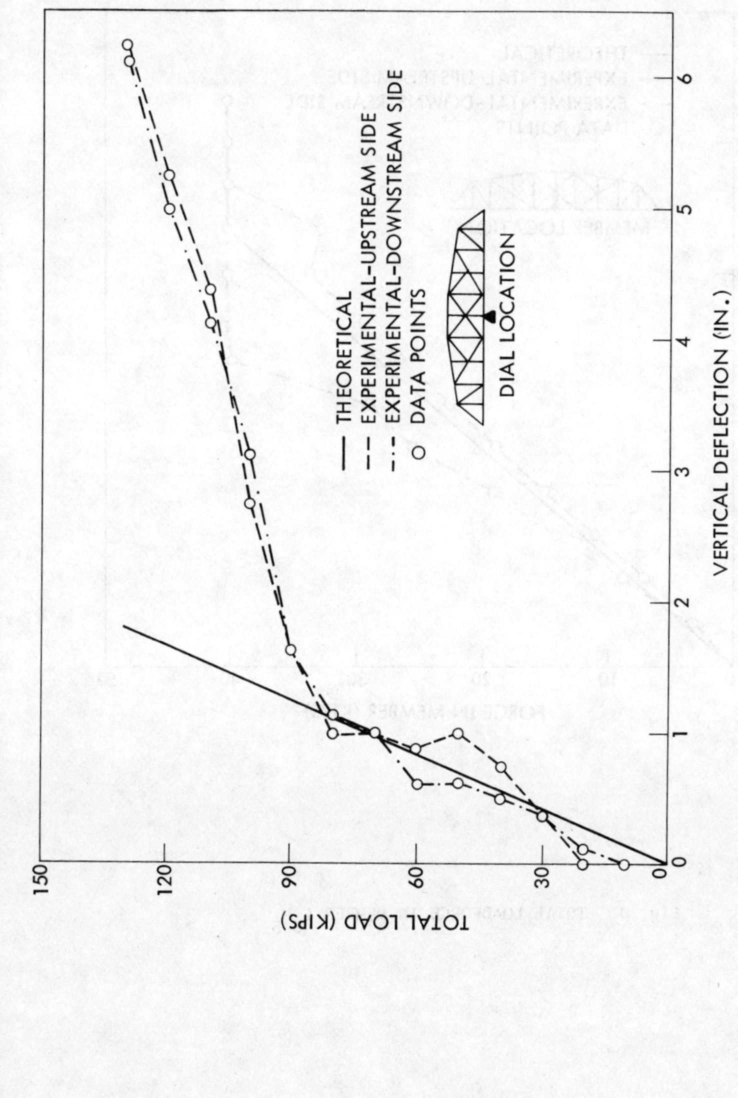

Fig. 39 TOTAL LOAD - VERTICAL DEFLECTION AT L_5 FOR TRUSS TEST

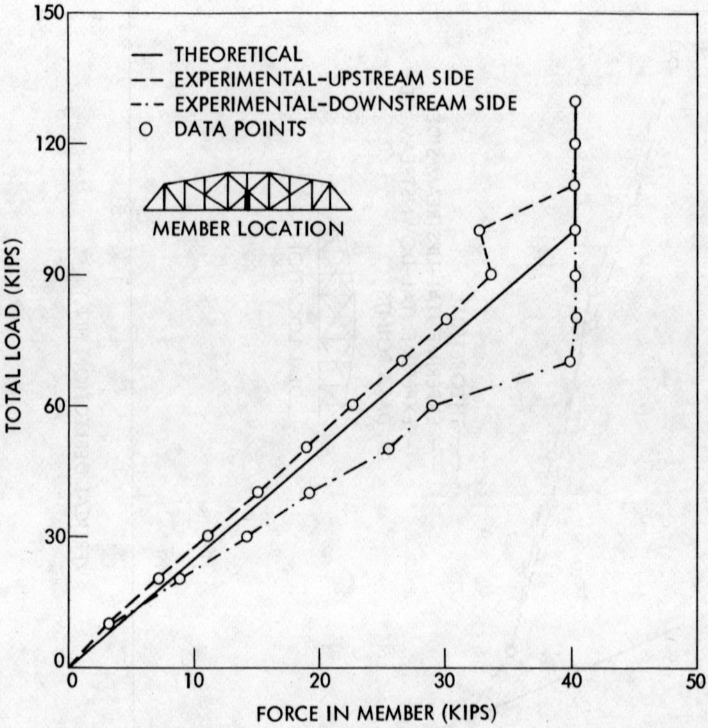

Fig. 40 TOTAL LOADFORCE IN MEMBER L_5M_5

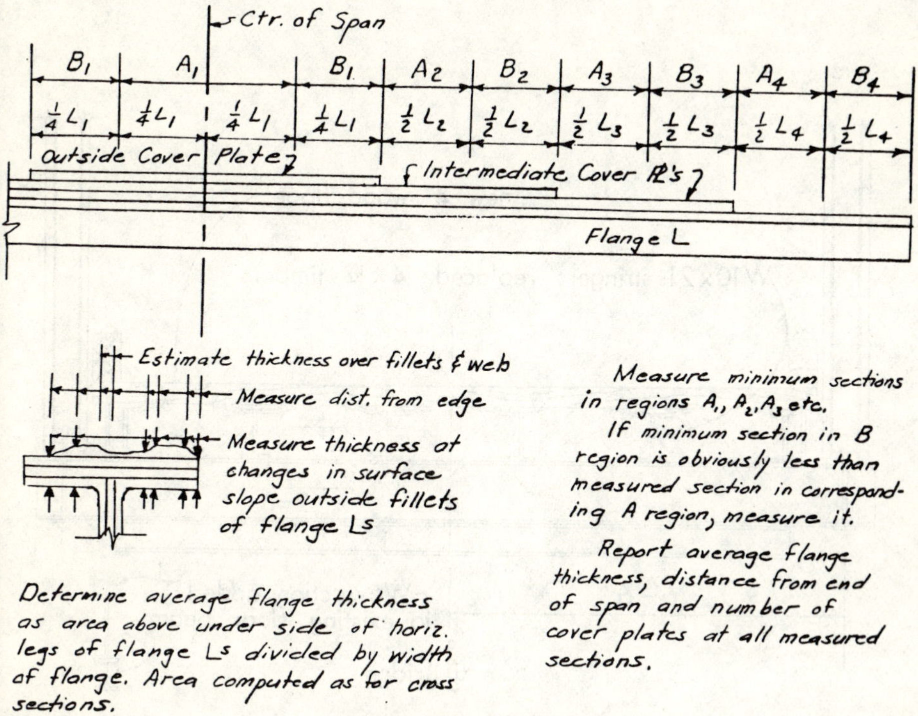

Fig. 41 INSTRUCTIONS FOR FLANGE MEASUREMENT OF COVER PLATED BEAMS

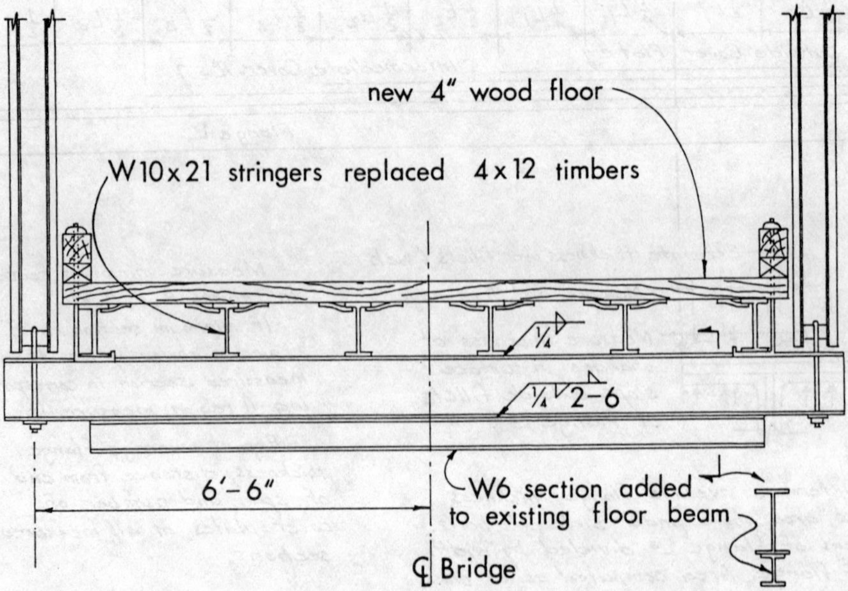

Fig. 42 STRENGTHENING SCHEME FOR FLOOR OF OLD TRUSS

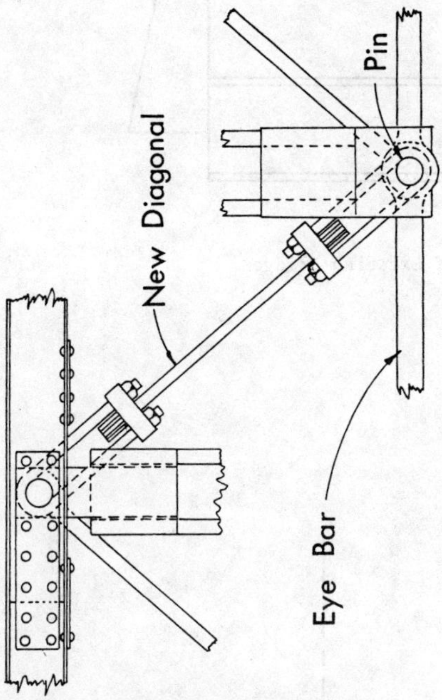

Fig. 43 REPLACEMENT DIAGONAL USED BY VIRGINIA

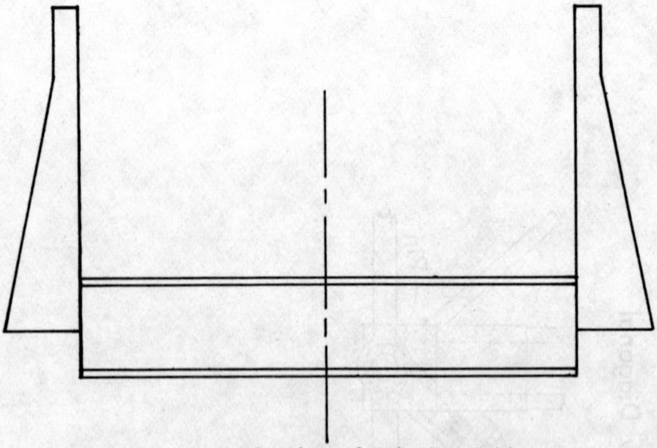

Cross Section of Existing Bridge

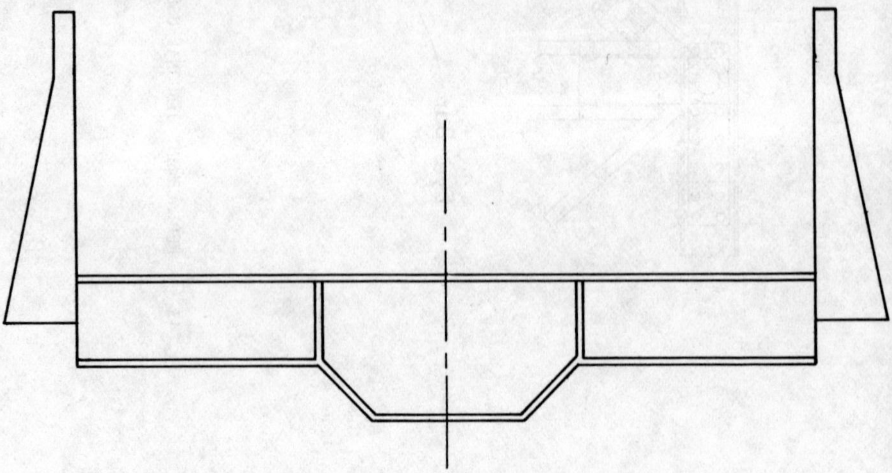

Cross Section of Widened Bridge

Fig. 44 WIDENING OF PONY TRUSS USING ROOR BEAMS

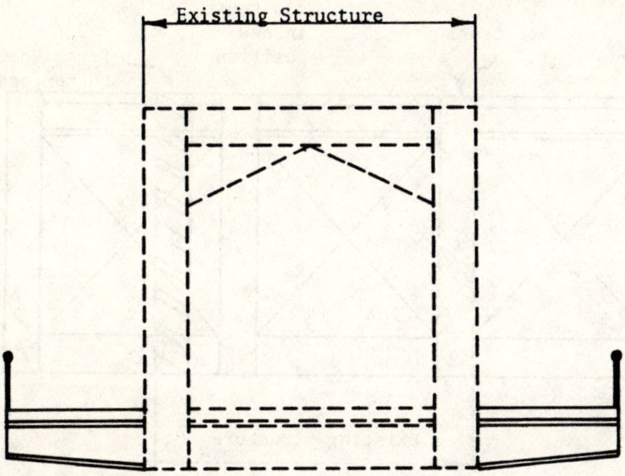

Fig. 45 WIDENING OF PONY TRUSS USING BRACKETS

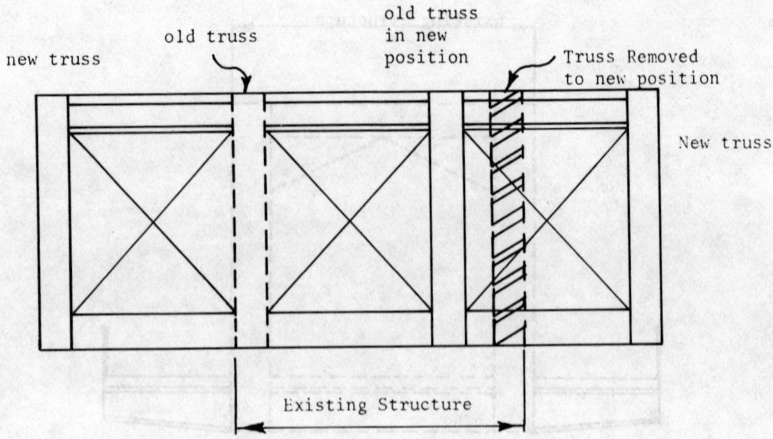

Fig. 46 WIDENING OF PONY TRUSS BY ADDING LONGITUDINAL TRUSSES

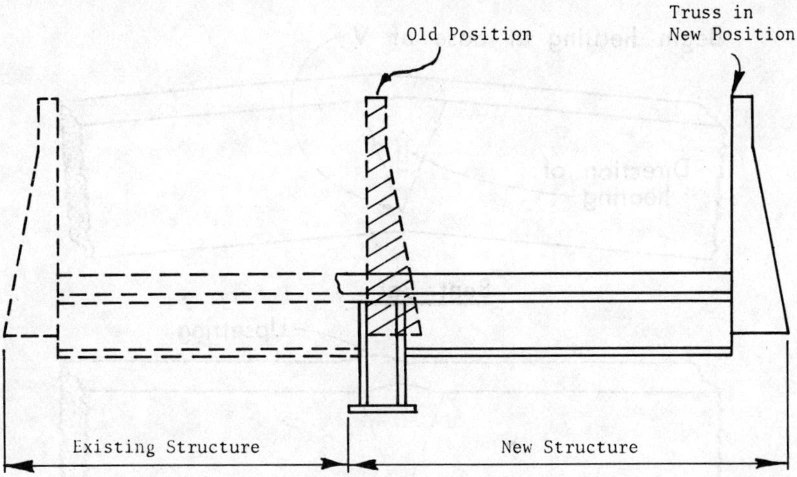

Fig. 47 WIDENING OF PONY TRUSS BY ADDING LONGITUDINAL GIRDERS

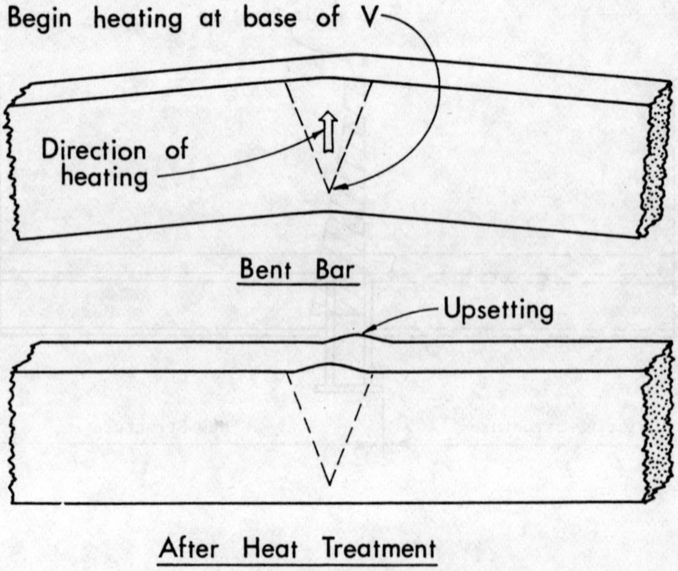

Fig. 48 HEAT STRAIGHTENING OF MEMBERS

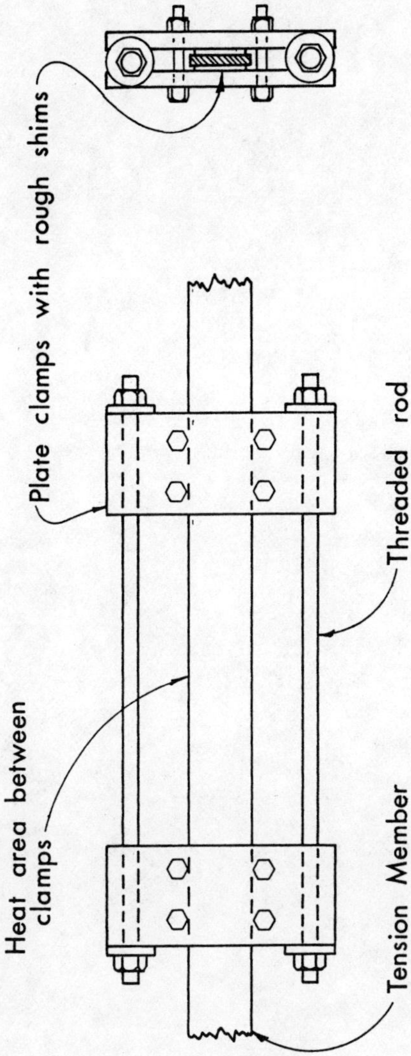

Fig. 49 YOKE FOR RESTORING TENSION TO MEMBERS BY UPSETTING HEATED AREA

(AFTER RECOMMENDATIONS BY CALIFORNIA DOT)

LIST OF TABLES

TABLE 1 - INSPECTION FORM FOR RAILWAY BRIDGES

(Name of Ry. Co.)
STEEL BRIDGE INSPECTION RECORD

Division ______
District ______
Bridge No. ______

Between Station(s): ______ State: ______ Tracks: ______

Waterway Roadway RR: ______ Center Ht: ______ Clearance: ______

Approaches: ______ Alignment: Tangent Spiral ______ Curve

Steel Spans: ______

Substructure: ______

Maintenance Responsibility: (Name) ______ Other (Specify) ______ Last SBF Insp: ______

CHECK LIST: ✓ – Satisfactory; X – Condition Requiring Comments; O – Not Applicable

DATE OF INSPECTION	Year / Month/Date											
TRACK (a-Approaches, b-Steel Span)						15. Truss Members						
1. Line and Surface						a. Chords, End Posts						
2. Running Rail (#)						b. Web Members – Vertical, Diagonal						
3. Anchorage : Fastenings						c. Pins, Connections, Splices						
4. Guard Rail (#)						d. Sway, Portal Bracing, Brackets						
5. Ties (Track, Bridge)						16. Lateral Bracing						
6. Ballast						17. Bearings						
DECK						SUBSTRUCTURE						
7. Deck (Timber, Steel, Concrete)						18. Bridge Seat, Caps						
8. Curb						19. Pedestals, Blocking						
9. Waterproofing						20. Abutments, Parapets, Wing Walls						
10. Apron Plates						21. Piers, Bents, Towers						
11. Hardware						22. Scour, Riprap						
12. Walk and/or Handrail						GENERAL						
SPAN						23. Paint, Protective Coating						
13. Floor System						24. Clearances						
a. Floorbeams (Flanges, Webs)						25. Channel, Waterway, Drift						
b. Stringers (Flanges, Webs)						26. Utilities, Attachments						
c. Bracing, Diaphragms, Connections						27. Inspection Facilities						
14. Main Beams/Girders						28. Damage – Rail, Highway, Water Traffic						
a. Flanges, Web, Stiffeners, Splices						29. Observation Under Traffic						
b. Cross Frames, Diaphragms, Brackets						30. Inspected by:						

ITEM	COMMENTS	PRIORITY	GANG	DONE

TABLE 2 - ULTIMATE STRENGTH OF CONCRETE SLABS

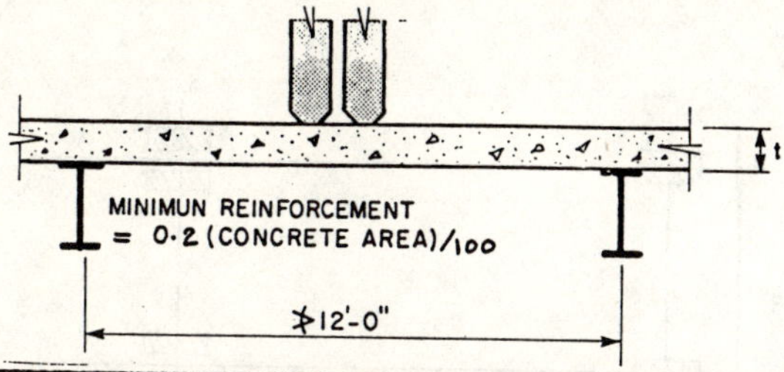

f'c psi	Minimum ultimate strength of concrete slabs in terms of a concentrated load, in kips, (representing contact area of one pair of wheels).									
	COMPOSITE CONSTRUCTION					NON-COMPOSITE CONSTRUCTION				
	6"	7"	8"	9"	10"	6"	7"	8"	9"	10"
3,000	70	100	135	175	220	35	60	80	105	140
4,000	80	125	170	220	275	45	70	100	130	170
5,000	105	150	205	270	330	55	85	120	160	205
6,000	125	180	245	310	390	65	100	140	185	230

t = thickness of competent material in the slab
f'c = compressive strength of concrete

TABLE 3 - TRUCK LOADING

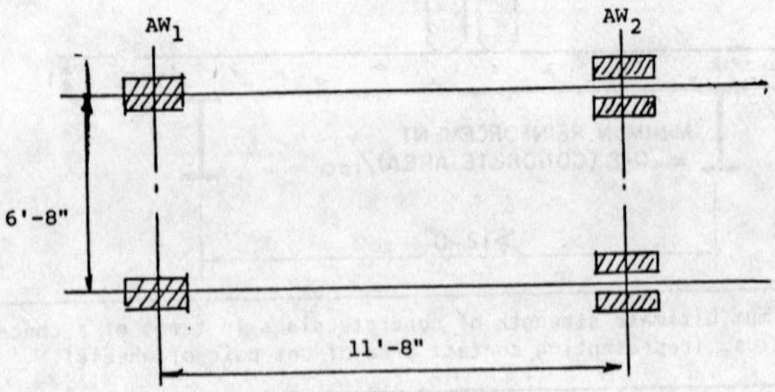

AXILE WEIGHT (lbs)

Bridge	AW1	AW2	Total Weight (lbs)
Longs Mill Rd	7960.	22740.	30700.
Crum Rd	7900.	22600.	30500.
Daysville Rd	7900.	22600.	30500.
Water Street Rd	7900.	22600.	30500.
Gapland	8100.	22300.	30400.
Hagerstown	8100.	22300.	30400.

TABLE 4 - EXPERIMENTAL FLOOR SYSTEM DATA

Load (kips)	Deck Without Nailers: Girder Stress 1,3	Girder Stress 2	Distribution % 1,3	Distribution % 2	Deck With Nailers: Girder Stress 1,3	Girder Stress 2	Distribution % 1,3	Distribution % 2
2	.90	4.2	15-15	70	---	---	---	---
4	1.5	6.5	15.5-15.5	69	3.0	6.0	25-25	50
6	2.4	12.6	14-14	72	---	---	---	---
8	3.0	18.0	12.5-12.5	75	4.8	9.9	24.5-24.5	51
10	3.9	21.6	14-14	72	6.6	16.5	22-22	56
12	4.5	24.0	14-14	72	7.5	20.4	21-21	58
14	---	---	---	--	8.4	24.9	20-20	60
16	---	---	---	--	10.2	33.0	19-19	62
17	---	---	---	--	13.5	36.0	21.5-21.5	57
	Average		14-14	72			22-22	56

<u>Distribution Factor</u>

Deck Without Nailers $\frac{S}{K} = .72$, $S = 3.0'$, $K = 4.2$

Deck With Nailers $\frac{S}{K} = .56$. $S = 3.0'$, $K = 5.4$

TABLE 5 - PROGRAM DATA DESCRIPTION

NAME	SOURCE	DESCRIPTION	DATA AVAIL	COMPUTER	LANGUAGE
BRASS	Wyoming State Highway Department	User may design, review or load rate structure. Load rating portion of the section analysis component load rates on shears, flexural stresses and bearing stresses using working stress method.	9/73	IBM 360/40	FORTRAN IV
BARS	Control Data Corporation	The system can perform the inventory and operating rating required by AASHO specifications and the posting rating and special permit analysis required by state law using working stress method.	3/92	IBM 360/50 CDC 6600 (IBM360/50 with secondary storage position) (IBM1130 Remote)	FORTRAN IV
BRRAT	Pennsylvania Department of Transportation	This program calculates Inventory, Operating and Safe Load capacity. Ratings on flexural stresses using working stress method.			FORTRAN IV

TABLE 6 - PROGRAM DATA DETAILS

NAME	BRIDGE TYPE								CONSTRUCTION MATERIAL						GENERAL CAPABILITY			
	CONCRETE SLAB	CONCRETE T-BEAM	STEEL GIRDER	STRINGER FLOOR BEAM	TRUSS	BOX CULVERTS	RIGID FRAME	SLANT LEG	STRUCTURAL STEEL	REINFORCED CONCRETE	COMPOSITE STEEL	PRESTRESS CONCRETE	COMPOSITE PRESTRESS	TIMBER	ANALYSIS	DESIGN	RATING	ROUTING
BRASS	X*	X*	X	O	O	X	X	X	X	X	X	O	O	X	X	X	X	O
BARS	X	X	X	X	X*	O	O	O	X	X	X	X	X	O	X	O	X	O
BRRAT	X*	X*	X	X	X*	O	O	O	X	X	X	O	O	O	X	O	X	O
OVLOAD	X	O	X	O	X	O	O	O	N	N	N	N	N	N	O	O	X	X
Maryland	O	O	X	O	O	O	O	O	X	O	X	O	O	O	X	X	X	O

*Limited to single span

N = Not knowing what kind of material, mass storage only provided section properties.

TABLE 7 - ANALYSIS CAPABILITY

NAME	SIZE LIMITS			METHOD	LOAD TYPE					GENERAL CAPABILITY							
	NUMBER SPANS	NUMBER JOINTS	NUMBER MEMBER		MAX NO LIVE LOAD	STANDARD AASHTO LL	SPECIAL & GENERAL TRUCK CONFIGURATION	LOAD TRAIN	SIDEWALK LL	CANTILEVERS	HINGES	NONPRISMATIC MEMBER	FLANGE TRANSITION	COMPOSITE OR NONCOMPOSITE	LOAD FACTOR METHOD	WORKING STRESS METHOD	TAPERED SECTION
BRASS	19	20/span	18/span	Column analogy Slope deflection	24	X	X	X	X	O	O	G	O	X	O	X	O
BARS	6	10/span	--	Matrix method	6	X	O	O	O	O	X	G	O	X	O	X	O
BRRAT	8	80	80		8	X	X	X	X	O	O	R	O	X	O	X	O
OVLOAD	50	50	50	Matrix stiffness method	50	X	X	X	O	O	O	R	O	O	O	X	O
Maryland	10	150	150	Matrix stiffness method	20	X	X	X	X	X	X	G	X	X	X	X	X

G = General; R = Restricted

TABLE 8 - AUTOMATIC CAPABILITY

NAME	LIVE LOAD								BRIDGE PROPERTIES					STRESSES			
	MOMENTS	SHEARS AND REACTION	DEFLECTION	IMPACT FACTOR	DISTRIBUTION FACTOR	SIDEWALK LL	MOMENT CRITICAL POINT	SHEAR CRITICAL POINT	COMPOSITE	NONCOMPOSITE	STANDARD SECTION TABLE	PLATE GIRDERS	SECTION PROPERTIES	YIELD STRESS FOR STEEL	INVENTORY RATING	OPERATING RATING	LOAD FACTOR METHOD
BRASS	X	X	X	S	I	I	X	X	X	X	O	X	IS	I	I	I	O
BARS	X	O	O	IS	S	O	X	O	X	X	X	X	IS	I	S	S	O
BRRAT	X	O	O	IS	I	I	X	O	X	X	O	X	I	I	S	S	O
OVLOAD	X	X	O	O	O	O	X	O	O*	O*	O*	O*	S	O*	S**	S**	O
Maryland	X	X	X	IS	IS	IS	X	X	X	X	X	X	S	I	IS	IS	X

I = Input, S = Self generated, IS = Input of self generated

* = Section properties were stored in mass storage beforehand

**Overload moment compared with standard HS load moment